IMPACT
CALIFORNIA
SOCIAL STUDIES

INQUIRY JOURNAL

WORLD
HISTORY & GEOGRAPHY

ANCIENT CIVILIZATIONS

Jackson J. Spielvogel, Ph.D.

Mc
Graw
Hill

mheducation.com/prek-12

Send all queries to
McGraw-Hill Educatio
8787 Orion Place
Columbus, OH 4324

ISBN: 978-0-07-906349-6
MHID: 0-07-906349-7

Printed in the United States of Americ

8 9 10 11 12 13 WEB 25 24 23 22 21 20

Table of Contents

Dear Student,

Most of us are curious, and we have questions about many things. We have the more personal questions, such as, "Will my favorite book be made into a movie?" or "Why does my former best friend not want to hang out with me anymore?" to questions of a larger nature about the world around us. These might include questions such as, "What does being treated like an adult mean?" "Why can't people share?" "Why do we have to go to war?" "How do I understand what I see or read about in history, online, or in the news?" and "Why is the peace process so difficult?"

Asking good questions helps us take charge of our own learning. Learning to ask good questions is a process, as "yes" and "no" types of questions do not get us very far in discovering why events happened or why people feel as they do. Once we master this process, however, we become better thinkers and researchers and can find out more about subjects that interest us. Asking good questions is also important if we want to understand and affect the world around us.

In this book, as in other parts of this program, there will be "Essential Questions" that you will research. These types of questions concern all people – those who have lived, those who are living now, and those who will live in the future. Examples of these questions include: "How do new ideas change the way people live?" "What makes a culture unique?" "What characteristics make a good leader?" and "Why does conflict develop?" You will choose some of your own supporting questions to help you answer the Essential Question.

As you move through the study of history, you will be reading primary and secondary sources about a specific time period. Primary sources—whether they are diaries, poetry, letters, or artwork—were created by people who saw or experienced the event they are describing. Secondary sources—whether they are biographies, or history books, or your student text—are created after an event by people who were not part of the original event.

Once you have completed the readings and the text notes, there is a "Report Your Findings" project in which you answer the Essential Question. You will work on some parts of the project by yourself, and you will work on other parts of the project with your classmates. You will be given many opportunities to take informed action. This means that you will use what you have learned and apply it to a current issue in a way that interests you. You will share this information with other students or with people outside of the classroom.

CHAPTER

1

Early Humans and the Agricultural Revolution

ESSENTIAL QUESTION

How do people adapt to their environment?

Think about how this question might connect the earliest human societies and civilizations to civilization today.

TALK ABOUT IT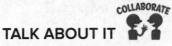

Discuss with a partner what type of information you would need to know to answer this question. For example, one question might be: How does understanding early human survival relate to people's struggles to survive today?

DIRECTIONS: Now write three additional questions that would help you to explain how the development of early humans led the way to civilization and to humans' continuing efforts to sustain a viable civilization.

MY RESEARCH QUESTIONS

Supporting Question 1:

_____

_____

Supporting Question 2:

_____

_____

Supporting Question 3:

_____

_____

The First Humans

DIRECTIONS: Search for evidence in Chapter 1, Lesson 1 to help you answer the following questions.

1A COMPARING AND CONTRASTING How are apes and monkeys alike and different? Fill in the chart to show similarities and differences.

Apes	Both	Monkeys

_____

_____

_____

_____

_____

_____

1B MAKING INFERENCES How do you think differences between apes and monkeys affected how they adapted to their environment?

_____

_____

_____

_____

1C IDENTIFYING CAUSE AND EFFECT Identify the impact of finding early fossils—human skulls and footprints—on how we understand the origin of the human species.

_____

_____

_____

ESSENTIAL QUESTION

How do people adapt to their environment?

As you gather evidence to answer the Essential Question, think about:

- what the earliest evidence showed about humans' origins.
- what enabled humans to grow and change over time.

My Notes

_____

_____

_____

_____

_____

_____

_____

2A **CITING TEXT EVIDENCE** The brain size of *hominins* led to the development of the *Homo* species and the way it interacted with the environment. What evidence from the text supports this statement?

_____

_____

_____

_____

_____

2B **IDENTIFYING CAUSE AND EFFECT** How did the development of larger brains lead to *Homo erectus* migrating out of Africa?

_____

_____

_____

_____

_____

_____

3 **MAKING INFERENCES** How do you think *Homo sapiens'* lighter, less-muscled body type led to its success over larger species?

_____

_____

_____

_____

4 **CITING TEXT EVIDENCE** Which migration theory—the Out-of-Africa model or the Multiregional Model—do you most agree with? Provide evidence from the text to support your answer.

_____

_____

_____

_____

Copyright © McGraw-Hill Education; Leakey, Richard. 2008. The Origin of Humankind. New York: Basic Books.

ESSENTIAL QUESTION
*How do people adapt to
their environment?*

VOCABULARY

innovation:
advancement

oblivion: nothingness

bipedal: having two
legs or feet

bestowed: gave

Richard Leakey on Human Origins

DIRECTIONS: Read the following excerpt and answer the accompanying questions.

EXPLORE THE CONTEXT Richard Leakey is the son of Mary and Louis Leakey, archaeologists famous for their work on early humans. Like his parents, Leakey studies human origins. Through his own archaeology work and his study of the work of others, he has expanded our understanding of how the first humans developed. In this excerpt, Leakey explores the role of the environment in evolution.

SECONDARY SOURCE: BOOK

❝Biologists have come to realize that mosaic environments of this kind, which offer many different kinds of habitat, drive evolutionary innovation. Populations of a species that once were widespread and continuous may become isolated and exposed to new forces of natural selection. Such is the recipe for evolutionary change. Sometimes that change is toward oblivion, if favorable environments disappear. This, clearly, was the fate of most of the African apes: just three species exist today—the gorilla, the common chimpanzee, and the pygmy chimpanzee. But while most ape species suffered because of the environmental shift, one of them was blessed with a new adaptation that allowed it to survive and prosper. This was the first bipedal ape. Being bipedal clearly bestowed important survival advantages in the changing conditions.❞

— Richard Leakey, *The Origin of Humankind,* 1994 C.E.

1 IDENTIFYING CAUSES According to the excerpt, what is "the recipe for evolutionary change"?

_____

_____

2 EXPLAINING EFFECTS How did environmental changes affect the evolution of African ape populations? What evidence does the author provide to support this conclusion?

_____

_____

_____

_____

_____

_____

3 INFERRING According to the excerpt, "Being bipedal clearly bestowed important survival advantages in the changing conditions." What do you think those advantages were?

_____

_____

_____

_____

_____

_____

4 GEOGRAPHY Based on this passage, how do you think the environment contributed to the development of hominins and early humans?

_____

_____

_____

_____

_____

_____

ESSENTIAL QUESTION
How do people adapt to their environment?

As you gather evidence to answer the Essential Question, think about:

- how technology changed ways in which Paleolithic people existed in their environments.
- the effects of the Ice Ages on human migration.

My Notes

_____

_____

_____

_____

_____

_____

_____

Hunter-Gatherers

DIRECTIONS: Search for evidence in Chapter 1, Lesson 2 to help you complete the following items.

1 DESCRIBING During the Paleolithic Age, what roles did men and women play within each group to contribute to the survival of the group?

_____

_____

_____

_____

_____

_____

_____

2 HISTORY How did the Ice Ages lead to the spread of humans from Europe and Asia into North and South America?

_____

_____

_____

_____

_____

_____

_____

_____

_____

3 **SUMMARIZING** Answer the questions in each box. Then use your answers to summarize how Paleolithic people adapted for survival.

A. What kinds of tools and weapons did Paleolithic people make? How did they use them?

_____

_____

B. What kinds of shelters did Paleolithic people build or use, and why did they differ among groups?

_____

_____

_____

_____

C. How did use of fire change the lives of Paleolithic people?

_____

_____

_____

D. In what ways did Paleolithic people communicate?

_____

_____

E. Write a summary explaining how Paleolithic people adapted.

_____

_____

_____

The Role of Caves

Copyright © McGraw-Hill Education; Moyes, Holley. Edited 2014. Sacred Darkness: A Global Perspective on the Ritual Use of Caves. University Press of Colorado: Boulder, CO.

ESSENTIAL QUESTION
How do people adapt to their environment?

DIRECTIONS: Read the following excerpt written by an anthropological archaeologist and answer the accompanying questions.

EXPLORE THE CONTEXT Many archaeologists study caves because of the wealth of information they hold in artifacts and paintings. Archaeologist Holley Moyes explores caves as mysterious and sacred places. She has found many skeletons in the darkest parts of caves and became interested in why ancient people offered their sacrifices in these dark spaces.

SECONDARY SOURCE: BOOK

  ❝For over a century, the idea of living in caves has gripped the imagination of scholars and the general public to the point that, in popular culture, the term cave man has become synonymous with early humans. This is not surprising when we consider that European caves produced some of archaeology's seminal finds. . . . Much of the earliest evidence for the antiquity of man came from European caves in which Pleistocene mammal bones co-occurred with stone tools.❞

—Holley Moyes, *Sacred Darkness: A Global Perspective on the Ritual Use of Caves,* 2012 C.E.

VOCABULARY

anthropology: the study of human society and culture
archaeologist: a person who studies material remains to learn about the past
seminal: an important part of a work that influences other parts of the work

antiquity: the long-ago past
Pleistocene: the geological period from about 2,588,000 to 11,700 years ago

1 ANALYZING Why do you think the author establishes the geographic location of the caves in this excerpt?

_____

_____

_____

_____

2 **CITING TEXT EVIDENCE** What does the author mean by saying caves have "gripped the imagination of scholars and the general public"?

_____

_____

_____

_____

3 **EXPLAINING** How does the author provide clues to the meaning of the word _seminal?_

_____

_____

_____

_____

4 **ANALYZING** Based on this excerpt, what is the author's purpose for writing this book?

_____

_____

_____

_____

5 **HISTORY** How does this excerpt help the reader know more about human ancestors?

_____

_____

_____

_____

Early Tools

ESSENTIAL QUESTION

How do people adapt to their environment?

DIRECTIONS Examine the images and then answer the accompanying questions.

EXPLORE THE CONTEXT: This photo shows two axe heads at left and other stone tools from the Paleolithic era. The Paleolithic era lasted from about 40,000 B.C.E. to 20,000 B.C.E.

PRIMARY SOURCE: ARTIFACTS

 DESCRIBING How did early humans use these tools?

_____

_____

_____

_____

2 **EXPLAINING EFFECTS** How did these tools help early humans survive their environment?

_____

_____

_____

_____

_____

3 **EXPLAINING** Explain how stone and fire helped early humans become a social group.

_____

_____

_____

_____

_____

_____

_____

4 HISTORY What is one important way stones contributed to early humans' survival? Support your answer using information from the photograph.

_____

_____

_____

_____

_____

The Agricultural Revolution

DIRECTIONS: Search for evidence in Chapter 1, Lesson 3 to help you complete the following items.

1 **HISTORY** Use the web organizer below to show changes and advances in people's way of life during Neolithic times.

ESSENTIAL QUESTION

How do people adapt to their environment?

As you gather evidence to answer the Essential Question, think about:

- how farming changed the ways in which people lived.
- how peoples' communities changed as their way of life changed.

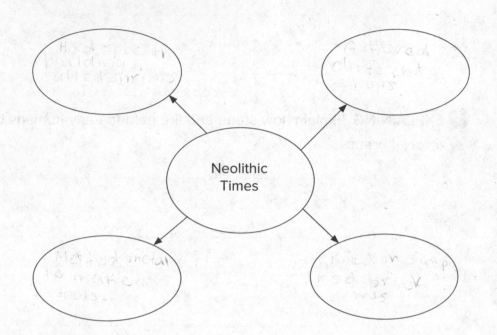

Neolithic Times

1A **CITING TEXT EVIDENCE** People in various parts of the world began planting different kinds of food crops. Complete the chart with examples of food grown in each region.

My Notes

_____

_____

_____

_____

_____

_____

_____

_____

_____

Region	Foods Grown
Southwest Asia	Teas and soybeans
Nile Valley	Millet, coffee, yams
Central Africa	Figs, sorghum, onions, wheat, and barley
India	wheat, barley, rice
China and Southeast Asia	Yams, sugar canes, soybeans, and rice
Mexico and Central America	cotton, beans, potatoes

2 INFERRING Why did people in Neolithic communities build permanent homes?

_____

_____

_____

3 CIVICS How did permanent settlements lead to job specialization among community members?

_____

_____

_____

4 DESCRIBING During the Bronze Age, civilizations began to develop, and all of these civilizations shared characteristics. Complete the chart below with details to illustrate each characteristic.

Characteristic	Details
Cities and Government	
Religions	
Social Structure	
Writing and Art	

Agriculture and Trade

ESSENTIAL QUESTION

How do people adapt to their environment?

DIRECTIONS: Read the excerpt and answer the accompanying questions.

EXPLORE THE CONTEXT: Geographer Lydia Mihelic Pulsipher is a cultural-historical geographer. She studies how people and geography affect each other in the present and the past. In this excerpt, she discusses the development of farming.

SECONDARY SOURCE: BOOK

" Why did agriculture and animal husbandry develop in the first place? Certainly the desire for more secure food resources played a role, but the opportunity to trade may have been just as important. Many of the known locations of agricultural innovation lie near early trade centers. There, people would have had access to new information and new plants and animals brought by traders, and would have needed products to trade. Perhaps, then, agriculture was at first a profitable hobby for hunters and gatherers that eventually, because of the desire for food security and market demands, grew into a "day job" for some—their primary source of sustenance. "

— Lydia Milhelic Pulsipher, *World Regional Geography: Global Patterns, Local Lives,* 2006 C.E.

VOCABULARY

husbandry: care of plants and animals

secure: reliable

"day job": familiar term for work that a person needs to pay everyday bills

sustenance: food needed for survival

1 IDENTIFYING CAUSES According to the author, why did early humans develop agriculture and animal husbandry?

_____

_____

2 ECONOMICS According to the excerpt, how did the Agricultural Revolution affect trade?

_____

_____

_____

3 ANALYZING How did the excerpt show that the Agricultural Revolution affected even the early humans' thinking?

_____

_____

_____

4 INFERRING Based on this excerpt, how did early humans adapt to their environment?

_____

_____

_____

Tools in the Bronze Age

DIRECTIONS: Examine the following image and answer the accompanying questions.

EXPLORE THE CONTEXT In the Bronze Age, early humans learned to mix copper with bronze. This mixture of metals made it easier for people to make very specialized objects—tools, weapons, and household goods—that were stronger and more durable. Bronze tools like these in the photo were used between 3000 and 1200 B.C.E.

PRIMARY SOURCE: ARTIFACTS

1 DESCRIBING What are these tools? How do you think they were used?

_____

_____

2 COMPARING AND CONTRASTING How are these tools similar to and different from the tools you analyzed in Lesson 2?

_____

_____

_____

3 EVALUATING EVIDENCE Why are these artifacts so important for the study of history?

_____

_____

_____

4 INFERRING How might these tools have changed the way early humans interacted with their environment?

_____

_____

_____

❶ Think About It

How did people adapt to their environment?

Review the supporting questions that you developed at the beginning of the chapter. Review the evidence that you gathered in Chapter 1. Were you able to answer each Supporting Question?

If there was not enough evidence to answer your Supporting Questions, what additional evidence do you think you need to consider?

_____

_____

_____

_____

❷ Organize Your Evidence

Use a chart to organize the evidence you will use to support your Position Statement. Think about the most basic ideas you had about early humans. Use the topics of the three lessons to come up with how your original ideas (column 1) changed into new ideas (column 3).

1	2	3
What I thought before lesson	Topics in lessons	What I know after lesson
	More like apes or monkeys?	
	Value of fossils	
	What does brain size have to do with it?	
	Homo sapiens	
	Making and using tools	
	Paleolithic hunters and gatherers	
	Nomadic lifestyle	
	Participation	
	Agricultural Revolution	
	System of farming	
	Trade increases	
	Growth of religion and art	

③ Write About It

Create a position statement focused on the ESSENTIAL QUESTION: *How did people adapt to their environment?* Use the evidence you gathered above to guide you in developing the statement.

_____

_____

_____

_____

_____

_____

_____

④ Talk About It

Work in small groups to present your position statement and evidence. Gather feedback from your classmates before you write your final conclusion. You may choose to refine your position statement after you have discussed it with your classmates. Group members should listen to each other's arguments, ask questions, and offer constructive advice.

⑤ Connect to the Essential Question

Develop a visual essay to present your position statement and the evidence you will use to support your position. Draw or choose photos and art from appropriate websites to illustrate the evidence. Include captions or short paragraphs explaining the evidence you present and how it helps support your position statement.

CITIZENSHIP
TAKING ACTION

MAKE CONNECTIONS For early humans, chances for survival improved when people lived in groups. Cooperation became a key part of everyday existence. Today, working together as a community is also important, both to push for change and to improve people's quality of life.

DIRECTIONS: Create a poster to hang in a public space. In your poster, use a combination of text and images to educate the public about the benefits of community involvement and cooperation.

_____

_____

_____

_____

_____

_____

_____

_____

_____

_____

_____

_____

_____

_____

Mesopotamia

ESSENTIAL QUESTION

How does geography influence the way people live?

Think about how this question might relate to the Sumerian city-states.

TALK ABOUT IT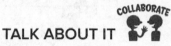

COLLABORATE

Discuss with a partner what type of information you would need to answer this question. For example, one question might be: Why did the geography of Mesopotamia encourage rivalries among the Sumerian city-states?

DIRECTIONS: Now write down three additional questions that would help you explain why the Sumerian cities became self-ruling, independent groups.

MY RESEARCH QUESTIONS

Supporting Question 1:

_____

_____

Supporting Question 2:

_____

_____

Supporting Question 3:

_____

ESSENTIAL QUESTION

How does geography influence the way people live?

As you gather evidence to answer the Essential Question, think about:

- the location of the first settlements between the Tigris and the Euphrates rivers.
- the Fertile Crescent, which is an area of rich farmland between the Mediterranean Sea and the Persian Gulf.

My Notes

_____

_____

_____

_____

_____

_____

_____

_____

The Sumerians

DIRECTIONS: Search for evidence in Chapter 2, Lesson 1 to help you answer the following questions.

1A **IDENTIFYING CAUSE AND EFFECT** How did Mesopotamia's geography attract settlements?

_____

_____

_____

_____

_____

1B **ANALYZING** What water supply challenges were faced by people who settled near rivers in Mesopotamia?

_____

_____

_____

_____

_____

2 **GEOGRAPHY** How did the geography of Mesopotamia contribute to Sumerian cities becoming independent city-states?

_____

_____

_____

_____

_____

3 IDENTIFYING CAUSE AND EFFECT Fill in the chart below to describe how the seasons affected the settlers' source of water. Describe how settlers responded to the changes.

Seasonal Changes in Water Supplies	People's Responses Over Time
SUMMER	
SPRING	

4 ECONOMICS Use the chart below to record the details of the effects of irrigation.

Some Results of Using Irrigation

An Early Chariot

DIRECTIONS: Examine the artifact below and answer the accompanying questions.

EXPLORE THE CONTEXT: The invention of the wheel changed the lives of Sumerians in important ways, such as transportation. This Sumerian artifact from around 2500 B.C.E. shows a wheeled chariot. Chariots were a form of transportation used by the Sumerians. A chariot driver stood above the axle and gripped his legs around a wooden centerpiece, which was often covered with fleece for comfort.

PRIMARY SOURCE: ARTIFACT

1 **DESCRIBING** Describe the mode of transportation shown and how it provided something more than a cart did. How do you think the drivers directed the donkeys or horses? What main advantage would chariot drivers have over cart users?

_____

_____

_____

_____

2 **ANALYZING** Who do you think would be the most likely users of chariots in Mesopotamia? Explain why you think so.

_____

_____

_____

_____

_____

3 **COMPARING** Does your analysis agree with the text description of the chariot's development and usage?

_____

_____

_____

_____

4 **HISTORY** How do you believe the invention of the chariot affected the culture at that time?

_____

_____

_____

_____

Sumerian Tools

DIRECTIONS: Study the following image and answer the accompanying questions.

EXPLORE THE CONTEXT: This image shows early Sumerian tools from around 2000 B.C.E. The Sumerians were the first people to put copper and tin together to make a beautiful and strong metal called bronze. Before they discovered bronze, some tools were made of clay.

PRIMARY SOURCE: ARTIFACTS

1 DESCRIBING Do you recognize the tools in the images? How do you think these tools were used?

_____

_____

_____

_____

_____

_____

2 HISTORY   In what ways do you think life changed for the Sumerians after these tools were created?

_____

_____

_____

_____

_____

_____

3 **ANALYZING TEXT EVIDENCE**   After referring to the text, describe what you know about the technology of toolmaking in Mesopotamia. What led to an improvement in tool making?

_____

_____

_____

_____

_____

_____

_____

4 **DRAWING CONCLUSIONS**   How do you think geography influenced the development of these tools?

_____

_____

_____

_____

_____

_____

_____

ESSENTIAL QUESTION

How does geography influence the way people live?

As you gather evidence to answer the Essential Question, think about:

- why the rulers desired more land.
- how empires developed through conquest.

My Notes

_____

_____

_____

_____

_____

_____

_____

Mesopotamian Empires

DIRECTIONS: Search for evidence in Chapter 2, Lesson 2 to help you answer the following questions.

1 HISTORY Use the chart to identify some results of the spread of empires in Mesopotamia.

Results of Empire Building

2 INTERPRETING Consider how the government of the Assyrian Empire was able to rule such a large area of land. What allowed for such an expansion of power?

_____

_____

3 CITING TEXT EVIDENCE Use the graphic organizer to cite reasons for the fall of the Assyrian Empire.

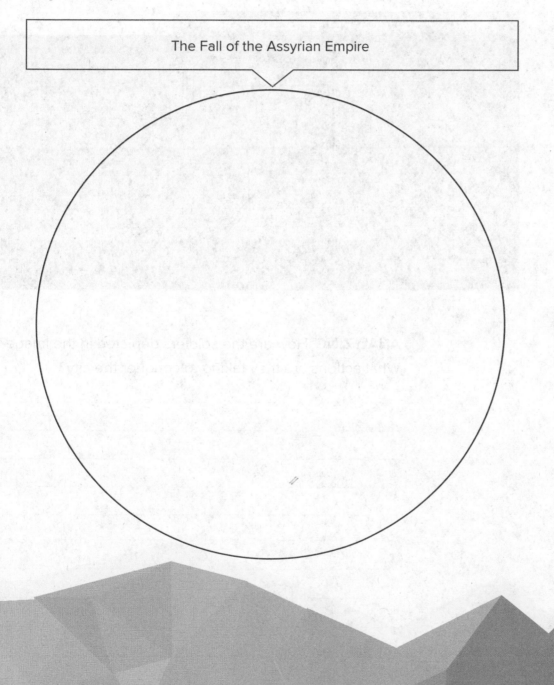

The Fall of the Assyrian Empire

Assyrians at War

DIRECTIONS: Examine the following image and answer the accompanying questions.

EXPLORE THE CONTEXT: A relief is a carving on a wall. The relief below is from Assyria's Central Palace, built around 728 B.C.E. This relief sculpture illustrates some early techniques and weapons that the Assyrians used to capture a city.

PRIMARY SOURCE: RELIEF SCULPTURE

1 ANALYZING How are the soldiers depicted in the image? What actions are they taking to conquer the city?

_____

_____

_____

_____

_____

_____

_____

_____

_____

_____

2 **DRAWING CONCLUSIONS** Why do you think cities were surrounded by tall walls wlth watchtowers? How would enemy soldiers get into the cities to conquer them?

_____

_____

_____

_____

_____

_____

3 **COMPARING AND CONTRASTING** Compare and contrast the text information describing the Assyrian army's weapons and actions with the image. How are the two alike and different?

_____

_____

_____

_____

_____

_____

4 HISTORY How did the attacks of the city-states change the lives of the conquered citizens? What were some of the effects after a new ruler was in charge?

_____

_____

_____

_____

_____

_____

Herodotus on Babylon

Copyright © McGraw-Hill Education; Herodotus. 1910 - Translated by George Rawlinson and Edited by E. H. Blakeney. The History of Herodotus - Volume One. London: J. M. Dent & Sons Ltd.; New York: E. P. Dutton & Co. Inc.

ESSENTIAL QUESTION

How does geography influence the way people live?

DIRECTIONS: Read the following excerpt and answer the accompanying questions.

EXPLORE THE CONTEXT: Herodotus was an early Greek historian who traveled and described the actions and sights he witnessed. This excerpt gives us a view of the defense system of the great city of Babylon.

PRIMARY SOURCE: EXCERPT FROM HERODOTUS 1:181: GREEK REPORTS OF BABLYLONIA, CHALDEA, AND ASSYRIA

"I.181: The outer wall is the main defense of the city. There is, however, a second inner wall, of less thickness than the first, but very little inferior to it in strength. The center of each division of the town was occupied by a fortress. In the one stood the palace of the kings, surrounded by a wall of great strength and size; in the other was the sacred precinct of Jupiter Belus [Bel], a square enclosure two furlongs each way, with gates of solid brass; which was also remaining in my time. In the middle of the precinct there was a tower of solid masonry, a furlong in length and breadth, upon which was raised a second tower, and on that a third, and so on up to eight. The ascent to the top is on the outside, by a path which winds round all the towers. When one is about halfway up, one finds a resting place and seats, where persons are wont to sit some time on their way to the summit. On the topmost tower there is a spacious temple, and inside the temple stands a couch of unusual size, richly adorned [decorated], with a golden table by its side. There is no statue of any kind set up in the place, nor is the chamber occupied of nights by any one but a single native woman, who, as the Chaldaeans, the priests of this god, affirm, is chosen for himself by the deity out of all the women of the land."

— Herodotus, *Histories,* c. 430 B.C.E.

VOCABULARY

precinct: a district or area

Jupiter Belus: a reference to the Akkadian God Bel

enclosure: an area shut in by walls or fences

furlong: a distance of approximately one-eighth of a mile, or 220 yards

masonry: something built with bricks or stones

breadth: width

wont: a habit or something a person is used to doing

chamber: a private room

1 **CITING TEXT EVIDENCE** According to Herodotus, which areas inside the city's walls received the most protection?

_____

_____

2 **DETERMINING MEANING** Examine the location of the temple room as described by Herodotus. Why would the location of the temple be important for Herodotus to describe in such detail?

_____

_____

_____

3 **CITING TEXT EVIDENCE** Which words did Herodotus use to describe how the city was protected against intruders? Underline the words he used.

_____

_____

_____

4 **HISTORY** Whose point of view does Herodotus use to explain the presence of the lady in the temple room?

_____

_____

_____

ESSENTIAL QUESTION

How does geography influence the way people live?

❶ Think About It

Review the Supporting Questions that you developed at the beginning of the chapter. Review the evidence that you gathered in Chapter 2. Were you able to answer each Supporting Question?

If there was not enough evidence to answer your Supporting Questions, what additional evidence do you think you need?

_____

_____

_____

_____

❷ Organize Your Evidence

Use the graphic organizer below to organize the evidence you will use to support your Position Statement.

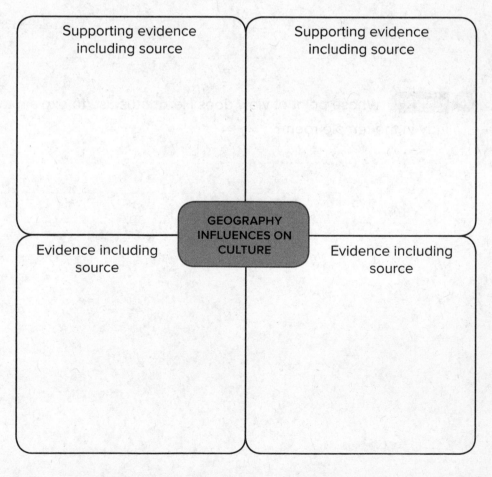

Supporting evidence including source

Supporting evidence including source

GEOGRAPHY INFLUENCES ON CULTURE

Evidence including source

Evidence including source

3 Write About It

A position statement related to the Essential Question should reflect your conclusion about the evidence. Write a Position Statement for the ESSENTIAL QUESTION: *How does geography influence the way people live?*

_____

_____

_____

_____

_____

_____

_____

_____

4 Connect to the Essential Question

On a separate piece of paper, create at least five good interview questions as if you were interviewing a person who lived in the Mesopotamian valley in one of the early Sumerian city-states. Think about asking why he or she settled where they did, what the advantages and disadvantages were, how they needed to adapt to the environment, etc.

After deciding what questions to ask, and using the Essential Question about geography's influence as your central idea, write how an early Sumerian might have answered your questions.

_____

_____

_____

CITIZENSHIP
TAKING ACTION

MAKE CONNECTIONS Think about how the geography of your region affects your home, family, and community. What are the natural resources in your area that affect the way you live?

DIRECTIONS: If geography and its natural resources are important in shaping the lives of people, how can you become involved in the care of it? If you need to, contact an organization you believe is helping care for your geographical resources. Ask if you can participate in some way. Then promote this need to other students using Twitter or other social media. (If you do not have a Twitter account, create a statement using only 140 characters to sell your idea to your friends.)

_____

_____

_____

_____

_____

_____

_____

_____

_____

_____

_____

_____

Ancient Egypt and Kush

ESSENTIAL QUESTION

Why do civilizations rise and fall?

Think about how this question might relate to civilization in the Nile River valley.

TALK ABOUT IT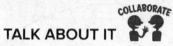

Discuss with a partner what type of information you would need to know to answer this question. For example, one question might be: How did the geography of the area encourage development along the Nile River in northeastern Africa?

DIRECTIONS: Now write down three additional questions that would help you explain why the Nile River valley became a desirable region for empire building.

MY RESEARCH QUESTIONS

Supporting Question 1:

_____

_____

Supporting Question 2:

_____

_____

Supporting Question 3:

_____

The Nile River

DIRECTIONS: Search for evidence in Chapter 3, Lesson 1 to help you complete the following items.

1 **DESCRIBING** Use the graphic organizer below to show ways the Nile River valley influenced the life of its early settlers.

ESSENTIAL QUESTION

Why do civilizations rise and fall?

As you gather evidence to answer the Essential Question, think about:

• the location of the first settlements near the Nile River.

• whether the river valley contributed to population growth.

Nile River Influence

Delta helped keep large body of water away
Red lands meant danger
Black land represented life
Cataracts made it difficut to travel by ship along the Nile

My Notes

_____

_____

_____

_____

_____

_____

_____

_____

2 **IDENTIFYING CAUSE AND EFFECT** What factors allowed the Egyptian civilization to develop peacefully?

The factors allowed Egyptian civilization's to develop peacfully because they had deserts which meant danger.

_____

_____

3 ECONOMICS How was the economy of Egypt influenced by the geography of the Nile River region?

The economy of Egypt influenced by the geography of the Nile region because the River helped them to keep other people out of Egypt, and they can also get buckets of water for farming.

4 HISTORY How did the Nile's predictable flooding help the people become resourceful and inventive? Use the graphic organizer below to organize the information.

The predictable river flooding helped them because it left behind silt which helped farmers grow crops.

```
                              ┌──────────────────────────────┐
                              │ In summer the Nile            │
                          ┌──▶│ would overflow banks.         │
                          │   └──────────────────────────────┘
┌──────────────┐         │   ┌──────────────────────────────┐
│              │─────────┤──▶│ In fall deposits of silt      │
│ Nile Flooding│         │   │ were left behind.             │
│              │         │   └──────────────────────────────┘
└──────────────┘         │   ┌──────────────────────────────┐
                          │   │ In dry seasons farmers        │
                          └──▶│ could use the Nile to         │
                              │ irrigate their crops.         │
                              └──────────────────────────────┘
```

A Shadoof

DIRECTIONS: Examine the image below and answer the questions.

EXPLORE THE CONTEXT: This image of a modern day shadoof shows a way that Egyptian farmers were able to fill the water basins used for irrigation of their fields. Irrigation revolutionized farming by helping the farmers control their water supply.

PRIMARY SOURCE: PHOTOGRAPH

1 **DESCRIBING** Describe the scene shown in the image.

_____

_____

_____

_____

_____

_____

2 ANALYZING CAUSE AND EFFECT How did climate affect the need for the creation of irrigation tools?

_____

_____

_____

_____

_____

3 IDENTIFYING EFFECTS How did people in the Nile River valley take advantage of annual flooding? How was the Nile easier to control than the Tigris and Euphrates Rivers?

_____

_____

_____

_____

_____

_____

4 EXPLAINING EFFECTS What was the effect of irrigation in the Nile River valley?

_____

_____

_____

_____

_____

_____

The Nile River

ESSENTIAL QUESTION

Why do civilizations rise and fall?

DIRECTIONS: Read the following excerpt and answer the questions.

EXPLORE THE CONTEXT: This excerpt from *The Nile Tributaries of Abyssinia and the Sword Hunters of the Hamran Arabs,* by Sir Samuel W. Baker, gives insight into the formation of the Nile River and its effect on the land that formed the delta region in Egypt.

VOCABULARY

affluents: streams of water flowing freely into larger streams or bodies of water
unnavigable: a stream not deep or wide enough for ships
Abyssinia: a region now known as Ethiopia, Africa

arteries: waterways
Blue Nile, Atbara: rivers in northeast Africa, both which flow into the Nile
inundates: to flood
inundation: a flooded condition
fertility: readiness to produce crops

1 DETERMINING MEANING Baker states that the two important rivers, the Blue Nile and the Atbara, change significantly due to rainfall. What causes this change, and why is this important?

_____

_____

_____

_____

_____

_____

SECONDARY SOURCE: BOOK

66 The two grand affluents of Abyssinia are, the Blue Nile and the Atbara, which join the main stream respectively in N. lat. 15 degrees 30 minutes and 17 degrees 37 minutes. These rivers, although streams of extreme grandeur during the period of the Abyssinian rains, from the middle of June until September, are reduced during the dry months to utter insignificance; the Blue Nile becoming so shallow as to be unnavigable, and the Atbara perfectly dry. At that time the water supply of Abyssinia having ceased, Egypt depends solely upon the equatorial lakes and the affluents of the White Nile, until the rainy season shall again have flooded the two great Abyssinian arteries. That flood occurs suddenly about the 20th of June, and the grand rush of water pouring down the Blue Nile and the Atbara into the parent channel, inundates Lower Egypt, and is the cause of its extreme fertility.

NOT only is the inundation the effect of the Abyssinian rains, but the deposit of mud that has formed the Delta, and which is annually precipitated by the rising waters, is also due to the Abyssinian streams, more especially to the river Atbara, which, known as the Bahr el Aswat (Black River), carries a larger proportion of soil than any other tributary of the Nile; therefore, to the Atbara, above all other rivers, must the wealth and fertility of Egypt be attributed.

It may thus be stated: The equatorial lakes FEED Egypt; but the Abyssinian rivers CAUSE THE INUNDATION."

— Sir Samuel W. Baker, *The Nile Tributaries of Abyssinia and the Sword Hunters of the Hamran Arabs*, 1867 C.E.

2 **ANALYZING** From this description, why did people choose to live near a changing water supply?

_____

_____

_____

_____

3 **EXPLAINING CAUSES** Reread Baker's description, and explain what caused the fertility of the delta.

_____

_____

_____

_____

4 ECONOMICS Describe how the Abyssinian streams affected the economic growth of the Nile River valley civilization.

_____

_____

_____

_____

_____

Life in Ancient Egypt

DIRECTIONS: Search for evidence in Chapter 3, Lesson 2 to help you answer the following question.

ESSENTIAL QUESTION

Why do civilizations rise and fall?

As you gather evidence to answer the Essential Question, think about:

- the power and authority of the Egyptian pharaohs.
- the role of religion in the life of the early Egyptians.
- the social groups in ancient Egypt and how they lived.

1 **CITING EVIDENCE** Use the graphic organizer below to identify ways the pharaoh influenced the Egyptian culture.

Pharaoh
_____
_____
_____
_____
_____

My Notes

_____
_____
_____
_____
_____
_____
_____
_____

2 **EXPLAINING CAUSE AND EFFECT** How did religion influence the culture of ancient Egypt?

_____
_____
_____
_____
_____
_____
_____
_____
_____
_____

3 DRAWING CONCLUSIONS Analyze the roles of Egyptians and their lifestyles. Is there a connection among jobs, social ranking, and lifestyle? Use the table to organize your answers.

JOB	SOCIAL RANK	LIFESTYLE
King/pharaoh	highest	

CONCLUSIONS:

ESSENTIAL QUESTION

Why do civilizations rise and fall?

The Gateway of the Temple of Edfu

DIRECTIONS: Study the following image and answer the accompanying questions.

EXPLORE THE CONTEXT: The Temple of Edfu, built between 237 and 57 B.C.E., gives insight about the lifestyle and the impact of religion on the culture of ancient Egyptians.

PRIMARY SOURCE: RELIEF SCULPTURE

 COMPARING AND CONTRASTING Compare the picture of the Temple of Edfu with the images of the pyramids in Lesson 2. Describe any similarities and differences you notice.

_____

_____

_____

_____

_____

_____

_____

2 DRAWING CONCLUSIONS Why would the Egyptians build enormous and elaborate temples and tombs? Cite text from Lesson 2 to support your conclusions.

_____

_____

_____

_____

_____

_____

_____

3 EVALUATING EVIDENCE Evaluate the images in the lesson and the text describing the roles of ancient Egyptians. Why were pharaohs and priests the most powerful and wealthy people in ancient Egypt?

_____

_____

_____

_____

_____

_____

_____

4 DRAWING CONCLUSIONS What does the ability to devote resources to building great monuments and temples suggest about the wealth and strength of an empire? Cite details from Lesson 2 to support your conclusions.

_____

_____

_____

_____

_____

Education in Ancient Egypt

DIRECTIONS: Study the following excerpt and answer the accompanying questions.

EXPLORE THE CONTEXT: In this excerpt, James Baikie describes a privileged Egyptian child who was being tutored, unlike most children of the early Egyptian times.

SECONDARY SOURCE: BOOK

66 When Tahuti grew a little older, and had fairly mastered the rudiments of writing, his teacher set him to write out copies of different passages from the best known Egyptian books, partly to keep up his hand-writing, and partly to teach him to know good Egyptian and to use correct language. Sometimes it was a piece of a religious book that he was set to copy, sometimes a poem, sometimes a fairy-tale. For the Egyptians were very fond of fairy-tales, and later on, perhaps, we may hear some of their stories, the oldest fairy-stories in the world. But generally the piece that was chosen was one which would not only exercise the boy's hand, and teach him a good style, but would also help to teach him good manners, and fill his mind with right ideas. Very often Tahuti's teacher would dictate to him a passage from the wise advice which a great King of long ago left to his son, the Crown Prince, or from some other book of the same kind. And sometimes the exercises would be in the form of letters which the master and his pupils wrote as though they had been friends far away from one another. Tahuti's letters, you may be sure, were full of wisdom and of good resolutions, and I dare say he was just about as fond of writing them as you are of writing the letters that your teacher sometimes sets as a task for you. 99

—James Baikie, *Peeps at Many Lands: Ancient Egypt*, 1916 C.E.

VOCABULARY

rudiments: basics
hand: refers to handwriting
dictate: to read aloud something for another person to transcribe, or write down

resolutions: deciding to take a certain action

1 **CITING TEXT EVIDENCE** Which sentences from this excerpt explain why early Egyptian students were required to copy text from books?

_____

_____

_____

2 **DRAWING CONCLUSIONS** What character qualities might a student gain from this type of educational experience?

_____

3 **DETERMINING CONTEXT** How do you think education may have contributed to a rise in Egypt's civilization?

_____

_____

_____

4 **ANALYZING POINT OF VIEW**

Discuss with a partner what you think the author wants you to know about Tahuti's attitude. What is the author suggesting about you and Tahuti as students then and now? Use evidence from the excerpt to support your answer.

_____

_____

_____

_____

5 **MAKING CONNECTIONS** If your teacher asked you to write letters to him or her about something you have read, what do you think the purpose would be?

_____

_____

ESSENTIAL QUESTION

Why do civilizations rise and fall?

As you gather evidence to answer the Essential Question, think about:

- the number of kingdoms flourished but yet declined.
- the growth and prosperity that resulted during established kingdoms.

My Notes

_____

_____

_____

_____

_____

_____

_____

_____

Egypt's Empire

DIRECTIONS: Search for evidence in Chapter 3, Lesson 3 to help you complete the following items.

1 **IDENTIFYING STEPS** Use the text and the graphic organizer below to identify what events led to the rise and fall of these kingdoms.

DATE	KINGDOM	EVENTS CAUSING RISE	EVENTS CAUSING FALL
2055 B.C.E.	MIDDLE KINGDOM		
1600s B.C.E.	HYKSOS		
1550 B.C.E.	THE NEW KINGDOM		

ANALYZING EVENTS Describe any patterns in the chart you made in the first question that might explain how a once flourishing kingdom could collapse.

_____

_____

_____

_____

3 ECONOMICS Using text evidence, how was the Egyptian economy affected by the change of kingdoms? Use the organizer below.

KINGDOM	ECONOMY
MIDDLE KINGDOM	
HYKSOS	
THE NEW KINGDOM	

Egyptian Pottery

ESSENTIAL QUESTION

Why do civilizations rise and fall?

DIRECTIONS: Study the following image and answer the accompanying questions.

EXPLORE THE CONTEXT: This image of two dishes, a bracelet, and a small box shows pottery from the New Kingdom period of ancient Egypt. The New Kingdom lasted from 1550 B.C.E. to 1070 B.C.E. Pottery from this period was made from a ground quartz and covered with a fired glaze that was most commonly blue or green in color. Vases, small animal and human figures, and decorative wall tiles were frequently made using this difficult technique.

PRIMARY SOURCE: ARTIFACT

1 CITING TEXT EVIDENCE Is there a connection between this period of empire building and Egypt's development in the arts? Cite the text reference from Lesson 3 and explain.

_____

_____

_____

_____

2 DESCRIBING Examine the details on the dishes and bracelet, and describe them. What do the designs reveal about Egyptian life? Explain.

_____

_____

_____

_____

_____

3 INFERRING How might religious beliefs be reflected in pottery?

_____

_____

_____

_____

4 ECONOMICS How did the economy impact the development of pottery?

_____

_____

_____

_____

Egyptian Tomb Complex

DIRECTIONS: Study the following image and answer the accompanying questions.

EXPLORE THE CONTEXT: The Middle Kingdom, which lasted from about 2055 B.C.E. to 1650 B.C.E., was a time of growth and prosperity for Egypt. During this time, the arts and literature flourished. This era also brought forth historic and massive building projects, which included burial tombs. Pyramids were still built. Other types of monuments, however, such as this one seen in this modern day photo, were being built for the dead.

PRIMARY SOURCE: PHOTOGRAPH

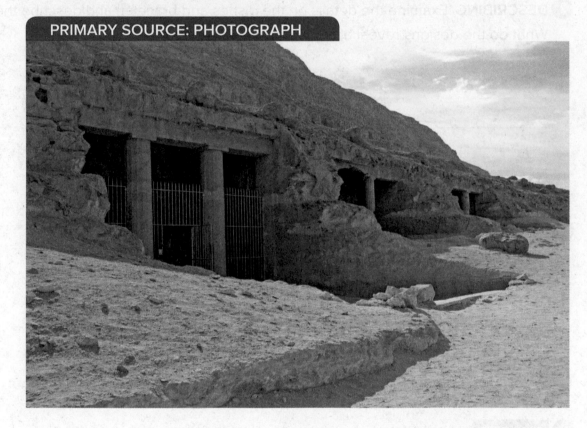

1 **SUMMARIZING** List three facts you learned in Chapter 3 about pyramids.

_____

_____

_____

_____

_____

2 **DESCRIBING** Describe the image of the tomb and its entrance.

_____

_____

_____

_____

3 **COMPARING AND CONTRASTING** Using what you learned about pyramids, how does the landscape around this tomb compare to the landscape around the pyramid? How are the pyramids and the Middle Kingdom tombs alike? How would the challenges of building tombs into the cliffs differ from the challenges of building a pyramid?

_____

_____

_____

_____

_____

_____

_____

4 GEOGRAPHY How did Egyptians make use of the different physical landscapes for their benefit?

_____

_____

_____

ESSENTIAL QUESTION

Why do civilizations rise and fall?

As you gather evidence to answer the Essential Question, think about:

- how Egypt influenced the kingdoms they conquered.
- why the Nubians grew wealthy and powerful.

My Notes

The Kingdom of Kush

DIRECTIONS: Search for evidence in Chapter 3, Lesson 4 to help you answer the following questions.

1 **EXPLAINING CAUSE AND EFFECT** How did Nubia grow wealthy?

_____

_____

_____

2 **GEOGRAPHY** How did the Egyptian culture influence the Nubian and Kush cultures?

_____

_____

_____

_____

_____

_____

_____

_____

_____

3 ANALYZING INFORMATION What did Nubia and Kush adopt from Egyptian culture? Use the chart to answer this question with details.

Nubians	Adopted From Egyptian Culture
Kushites	Adopted From Egyptian Culture

Nubia and Kush

DIRECTIONS: Study the following excerpt and answer the accompanying questions.

EXPLORE THE CONTEXT: Nubia and Kush were thriving civilizations in Africa, located just south of Egypt. As empires spread, it was logical that these kingdoms near the Nile would be targets for conquest. Kush and Nubia were prosperous, with fertile land and gold to be mined. The following excerpt is from the story of a sailor, written about 2200 B.C.E., who claimed to have been shipwrecked on an island in or near Punt, which was located along the coast of modern-day Ethiopia and Djibouti. The story may be fiction, but the resources noted were items Egyptians received from trade with Nubians and the land of Punt.

PRIMARY SOURCE: STORY

66 Let thy heart be satisfied, O my lord, for that we have come back to the country...Moreover, we have come back in good health, and not a man is lacking; although we have been to the ends of Wawat [Nubia], and gone through the land of Senmut [Kush], we have returned in peace, and our land—behold, we have come back to it. ...

They had said that the wind would not be contrary, or that there would be none. But as we approached the land, the wind arose, and threw up waves eight cubits high. As for me, I seized a piece of wood; but those who were in the vessel perished, without one remaining. A wave threw me on an island, after that I had been three days alone, without a companion beside my own heart. I laid me in a thicket, and the shadow covered me. Then stretched I my limbs to try to find something for my mouth. I found there figs and grain, melons of all kinds, fishes, and birds. Nothing was lacking. And I satisfied myself; and left on the ground that which was over, of what my arms had been filled withal. I dug a pit, I lighted a fire, and I made a burnt offering unto the gods...

Then I bowed myself before [a serpent calling himself the Prince of Punt], and held my arms low before him, and he, he gave me gifts of

VOCABULARY

contrary: hostile, causing problems

cubits: a cubit was the length of the forearm, 17–21 inches

thicket: underbrush, bushes

withal: with it all

burnt offering: a ritual to honor the Gods

. . . continued

precious perfumes, of cassia, of sweet woods, of kohl, of cypress, an abundance of incense, of ivory tusks, of baboons, of apes, and all kinds of precious things. **"**

—from *The World's Story: A History of the World in Story, Song And Art,* 1914 C.E.

1 DETERMINING POINT OF VIEW

Discuss with a partner the tone of the traveler who is discussing his journey. Does he suggest he is angry about the experience, amazed at his findings, relieved that it is over, or some other emotion? Use evidence from the text to support your answers.

_____

_____

_____

_____

2 DRAWING CONCLUSIONS What does the writer suggest about Egypt's relationship with Kush and Nubia?

_____

_____

3 MAKING CONNECTIONS If you had been shipwrecked and later wrote about your experience, what do you think would be the most important detail to describe?

_____

_____

4 INFERRING Consider how the traveler refers to Nubia and Kush. What can you infer from the way he talks about these empires?

_____

_____

_____

_____

Herodotus on Ethiopia

Copyright © McGraw-Hill Education; Herodotus. Translated by George Rawlinson. The History of Herodotus - Volume II. Reprinted 1909 in The Historians of Greece - Vol. II. New York: The Tandy-Thomas Company.

ESSENTIAL QUESTION

Why do civilizations rise and fall?

DIRECTIONS: Study the following excerpt and answer the questions.

EXPLORE THE CONTEXT: Herodotus was an ancient Greek historian who traveled the ancient world, observing the lives of people and recording his reflections in narrative, or story form. He writes about the region south of Egypt in eastern Africa known as Ethiopia in this narrative.

PRIMARY SOURCE: BOOK

"Where the south declines towards the setting sun lies the country called Ethiopia, the last inhabited land in that direction. There gold is obtained in great plenty, huge elephants abound, with wild trees of all sorts, and ebony; and the men are taller, handsomer, and longer lived than anywhere else. The Ethiopians were clothed in the skins of leopards and lions, and had long bows made of the stem of the palm-leaf, not less than four cubits in length. On these they laid short arrows made of reed, and armed at the tip, not with iron, but with a piece of stone, sharpened to a point, of the kind used in engraving seals. They carried likewise spears, the head of which was the sharpened horn of an antelope; and in addition they had knotted clubs. When they went into battle they painted their bodies, half with chalk, and half with vermilion. . . ."

—from *Herodotus: The Histories, Book III,* c. 430 B.C.E.

VOCABULARY

Ethiopia: once called Abyssinia, an ancient region in northeastern Africa that borders Egypt and the Red Sea

ebony: a heavy, black wood

cubits: a measurement taken with the forearm, about 17–21 inches long

reed: the straight stalk of a plant

vermilion: a bright red or orange-red color

1 CITING TEXT EVIDENCE Which sentences provide the best description of the Ethiopian people?

_____

_____

_____

2 COMPARING AND CONTRASTING How does the description of Ethiopia by Herodotus compare or contrast with the details about Nubia found in Lesson 4?

_____

_____

_____

3 DRAWING CONCLUSIONS What does this narrative suggest about the potential for this Ethiopian civilization?

_____

_____

_____

_____

4 DETERMINING CENTRAL IDEAS Herodotus describes Ethiopia as the last inhabited land in the direction of the setting sun. What do you think was the overall impression of Herodotus concerning this land? Write your understanding of the main idea below. Underline details that support your main idea.

_____

_____

_____

_____

_____

_____

① Think About It

Review the supporting questions you developed at the opening of the chapter. Review the evidence you found in Chapter 3. Were you able to answer each of your Supporting Questions?

If you didn't find enough evidence to answer your Supporting Questions, what do you think you need to consider?

_____

_____

_____

_____

② Organize Your Evidence

Use a chart like the one below to organize the evidence you will use to support your position statement. Then, create a position statement for the ESSENTIAL QUESTION: *Why do civilizations rise and fall?*

Sources of Information	Evidence from Sources to Cite	How the Evidence Supports your Position Statement

③ Talk About It

Discuss your position statement and the evidence you have gathered with a small group or partner. Check your group's understanding and answer any questions members may have. Consider any additional advice or input they may have.

④ Connect to the Essential Question

On a separate piece of paper, write an autobiographical journal entry from the viewpoint of a child living in Kush during the Middle Kingdom. As the son or daughter of a farmer, how did the rise of the Assyrian kingdom affect the way you and your family lived? Your journal page should include answers to the **ESSENTIAL QUESTION:** *Why do civilizations rise and fall?*

_____

_____

_____

CITIZENSHIP
TAKING ACTION

MAKE CONNECTIONS Many civilizations have risen and fallen during recorded history. These include Mesopotamia, Egypt, Rome, and the British Empire. Empires do not exist today in the same way they once did, although individual countries can have great influence over other countries, sometimes through economic policies, sometimes through military intervention. Syria is a country in Western Asia that formed as a modern nation after the end of World War II. In 2011 C.E., civil war broke out, with armed rebels seeking to remove the president. One of the country's largest cities, Aleppo, has been at the center of this conflict. Once a thriving metropolis, it has been largely destroyed. Many of the people who once lived there fled to other parts of the country or to other countries.

DIRECTIONS: Consider nations in the world that are in conflict today. Choose one conflict and research its causes and current status. Write a letter to your representative(s) to Congress outlining your position on the conflict. Suggest an action you would like that representative to take as a member of Congress.

_____

_____

_____

_____

_____

_____

_____

_____

CHAPTER

4

The Israelites, 1800 B.C.E. to 70 C.E.

ESSENTIAL QUESTION

How does religion shape society?

Think about how this question might connect the history of Israelite society and Judaism with the history and development of other religions.

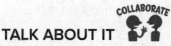

TALK ABOUT IT

Discuss with a partner what type of information you would need to know to answer this question. For example, one question might be: How does understanding religious practices and daily life in Israelite societies relate to modern religious practices and their effect on societies?

DIRECTIONS: Now write down three additional questions that you need to answer to be able to explain how the development of Judaism shaped daily life for the Israelites and led to practices in modern Judaism.

MY RESEARCH QUESTIONS

Supporting Question 1:

_____

_____

_____

Supporting Question 2:

_____

_____

Supporting Question 3:

_____

_____

ESSENTIAL QUESTION

How does religion shape society?

As you gather evidence to answer the Essential Question, think about:

- the stories of Abraham's interactions with God and of Abraham's descendants.
- the reactions of the Israelites to the new Pharaoh and to Moses.

My Notes

Beginnings

DIRECTIONS: Search for evidence in Chapter 4, Lesson 1 to help you answer the following questions.

1 **RELATING EVENTS** Which leaders led the Israelites first to Canaan, then to Egypt, and then out of Egypt and back to Canaan?

_____

_____

_____

_____

_____

_____

2 **EXPLAINING CAUSE AND EFFECT** How did the leaders of the Israelites know where to bring their people?

_____

_____

_____

_____

_____

_____

_____

_____

3 GEOGRAPHY In the graphic organizer below, write the name of the leader in each listed account from the Hebrew Bible. Then describe the influence the individual had on the way the Israelites lived.

Account in the Hebrew Bible	Influence on Israelites' Society
Journey to Canaan:	
Journey to Egypt:	
Journey Out of Egypt:	
Journey to Retake Canaan:	

4 ANALYZING EVENTS What religious belief inspired the Israelites under Joshua to fight to establish Canaan as their new homeland?

_____

_____

_____

_____

_____

_____

_____

_____

_____

_____

_____

_____

_____

5 **SUMMARIZING AND DESCRIBING** In the graphic organizer below, use your own words to provide the meaning of each of the commandments listed in the first column.

Commandment	Meaning
First Commandment	
Third Commandment	
Fifth Commandment	
Seventh Commandment	
Eighth Commandment	
Ninth Commandment	

The Birth of Isaac

ESSENTIAL QUESTION
How does religion shape society?

DIRECTIONS: Read the following excerpt and answer the accompanying questions.

EXPLORE THE CONTEXT: Abraham is considered to be the father of Judaism and Sarah its mother. According to the Hebrew Bible, Abraham and Sarah wanted children. This is the account of the beginning of their family and of the Israelites' family tree.

PRIMARY SOURCE: BOOK

❝ 21:1 And HaShem [God] remembered Sarah as He had said, and HaShem did unto Sarah as He had spoken.

21:2 And Sarah conceived, and bore Abraham a son in his old age, at the set time of which G-d had spoken to him.

21:3 And Abraham called the name of his son that was born unto him, whom Sarah bore to him, Isaac. . . .

21:5 And Abraham was a hundred years old, when his son Isaac was born unto him.

21:6 And Sarah said: 'G-d hath made laughter for me; every one that heareth will laugh on account of me.'

21:7 And she said: 'Who would have said unto Abraham, that Sarah should give [have] children? . . . for I have borne him a son in his old age.' ❞

—from the Hebrew Bible, Genesis 21:1–7

VOCABULARY

conceived: became pregnant

bore: gave birth

1 **DETERMINING MEANING** What is happening in this account from the Hebrew Bible?

_____

_____

_____

_____

2 INFERRING This account in Genesis says that God "did unto Sarah as He had spoken." Then Sarah became pregnant. What can you infer from this account about what God did for Sarah and why Sarah needed God's help?

_____

_____

_____

_____

3 CITING TEXT EVIDENCE What evidence in the text can you find for how Sarah feels about giving birth to Isaac? How does she feel about becoming a mother? Why is this birth unusual?

_____

_____

_____

_____

_____

_____

_____

_____

4 ANALYZING TEXT After Abraham died, his son Isaac and later his grandson Jacob headed the family. How does this account of Isaac's birth show that God of the Hebrew Bible was involved in what happened to the ancestors of the ancient Israelites?

_____

_____

_____

_____

God's Message to Joshua and the Israelites

ESSENTIAL QUESTION
How does religion shape society?

DIRECTIONS: Read the following excerpt and answer the accompanying questions.

EXPLORE THE CONTEXT: In the Hebrew Bible, the book of Joshua describes all of the ways in which God helped the Israelites through crises and provided for them. Joshua is said to have received this information from God, after which he related it to his people.

VOCABULARY

dwelt: lived in
plagued: set troubles upon

wilderness: unsettled area
labor: work

PRIMARY SOURCE: BOOK

"24:2 And Joshua said unto all the people, Thus saith the LORD God of Israel, Your fathers dwelt on the other side of the flood in old time, even Terah, the father of Abraham, and the father of Nachor: and they served other gods.

24:3 And I took your father Abraham from the other side of the flood, and led him throughout all the land of Canaan, and multiplied his seed, and gave him Isaac.

24:4 And I gave unto Isaac Jacob and Esau: and I gave unto Esau Mount Seir, to possess it; but Jacob and his children went down into Egypt.

24:5 I sent Moses also and Aaron, and I plagued Egypt, according to that which I did among them: and afterward I brought you out.

24:6 And I brought your fathers out of Egypt: and ye came unto the sea; and the Egyptians pursued after your fathers with chariots and horsemen unto the Red sea.

24:7 And when they cried unto the LORD, he put darkness between you and the Egyptians, and brought the sea upon them, and covered them; and your eyes have seen what I have done in Egypt: and ye dwelt in the wilderness a long season. . . .

24:11 And you went over Jordan, and came unto Jericho: and the men of Jericho fought against you, the Amorites, and the Perizzites, and the Canaanites, and the Hittites, and the Girgashites, the Hivites, and the Jebusites; and I delivered them into your hand.

24:13 And I have given you a land for which ye did not labor, and cities which ye built not, and ye dwell in them; of the vineyards and oliveyards which ye planted not do ye eat.

24:14 Now therefore fear the LORD, and serve him in sincerity and in truth: and put away the gods which your fathers served on the other side of the flood, and in Egypt; and serve ye the LORD. . .

24:24 And the people said unto Joshua, The LORD our God will we serve, and his voice will we obey. 🟦

—from the Hebrew Bible, Joshua 24:3–7, 11, 13–14, 24

1 **DETERMING MEANING** In the biblical account, what does God mean by "plagued Egypt" and why would he do such a thing?

_____

_____

_____

_____

_____

_____

2 **CITING TEXT EVIDENCE** What evidence can you find in the text of the miracle that Moses is said to have performed in order to rescue the Israelites? What did Moses do, and what happened to the Egyptians?

_____

_____

_____

_____

_____

_____

_____

_____

_____

_____

3 **ANALYZING EVENTS** Why does God tell the Israelites about all of the things he has done for their people? What goal is he trying to reach by sharing this information with them?

_____

_____

_____

_____

_____

_____

_____

_____

4 **ANALYZING IDEAS** How were the Israelites' ideas of worship similar to those of their ancestors two generations before?

_____

_____

_____

_____

_____

_____

_____

_____

ESSENTIAL QUESTION

How does religion shape society?

As you gather evidence to answer the Essential Question, think about:

- how King David and King Solomon were both able to keep the peace.

- how inability to overcome divisions led to the downfall of Israel, Judah, and the destruction of the First Temple.

My Notes

_____

_____

_____

_____

_____

_____

_____

The Israelite Kingdom

DIRECTIONS: Search for evidence in Chapter 4, Lesson 2 to help you answer the following questions.

1 ANALYZING INDIVIDUALS How did King David and King Solomon include Judaism as a part of their rule?

_____

_____

_____

_____

_____

_____

_____

_____

_____

_____

2 ANALYZING EVENTS How did the split between Israel and Judah lead to the downfall of both kingdoms?

_____

_____

_____

_____

_____

_____

3 **DESCRIBING** What role did the prophets play in the downfall of Judah?

_____

_____

_____

_____

_____

_____

_____

4 CIVICS In the graphic organizer below, in your own words, write the teachings of two of the Israelite Prophets as discussed in the text. Find examples in the text that show how people in Israelite communities were influenced by each prophet's teachings.

Prophet and Teaching	Example in Israelite Daily Life

King David and the Prophet Nathan

ESSENTIAL QUESTION
How does religion shape society?

DIRECTIONS: Read the following excerpt and answer the accompanying questions.

EXPLORE THE CONTEXT: King David took the attractive wife of one of his soldiers, a man named Uriah. He, then, assigned Uriah to a very dangerous military action. David knew this would result in Uriah's death. When he was killed, the prophet Nathan confronted David.

VOCABULARY

ewe: female sheep   *bosom:* chest
reared: raised   *dress:* prepare for cooking

PRIMARY SOURCE: BOOK

❝1 And HaShem [God] sent Nathan unto David. And he came unto him, and said unto him: 'There were two men in one city: the one rich, and the other poor.

2 The rich man had exceeding many flocks and herds;

3 but the poor man had nothing save one little ewe lamb, which he had bought and reared; and it grew up together with him, and with his children; it did eat of his own morsel, and drank of his own cup, and lay in his bosom, and was unto him as a daughter.

4 And there came a traveller unto the rich man, and he spared to take of his own flock and of his own herd, to dress for the wayfaring man that was come unto him, but took the poor man's lamb, and dressed it for the man that was come to him.'

5 And David's anger was greatly kindled against the man; and he said to Nathan: 'As HaShem liveth, the man that hath done this deserveth to die;

6 and he shall restore the lamb fourfold, because he did this thing, and because he had no pity.'

7 And Nathan said to David: 'Thou art the man. Thus saith HaShem, the G-d of Israel: I anointed thee king over Israel, and I delivered thee out of the hand of Saul;

8 and I gave thee thy master's house, and thy master's

wives into thy bosom, and gave thee the house of Israel and of Judah; and if that were too little, then would I add unto thee so much more.

9 Wherefore hast thou despised the word of HaShem, to do that which is evil in My sight? Uriah the Hittite thou hast smitten with the sword, and his wife thou hast taken to be thy wife, and him thou hast slain with the sword of the children of Ammon.

10 Now therefore, the sword shall never depart from thy house; because thou hast despised Me, and hast taken the wife of Uriah the Hittite to be thy wife. . . .

13 And David said unto Nathan: 'I have sinned against HaShem.' And Nathan said unto David: 'The HaShem also hath put away thy sin; thou shalt not die. 99

—from the Hebrew Bible, II Samuel 12:1–10, 13

IDENTIFYING Which of the Ten Commandments did David break by taking Uriah's wife and putting Uriah in a situation in which David knew Uriah would be killed? How did his actions go against these commandments?

_____

_____

_____

_____

_____

_____

_____

2 **DESCRIBING** How does the excerpt help you to understand David as a ruler of the Israelites?

_____

_____

_____

_____

_____

_____

_____

_____

Isaiah's Message to the
Israelites (Give the Hungry
and the Poor

3 **CITING TEXT EVIDENCE** What evidence in the text can you find for David's recognition of wrong action?

_____

_____

_____

_____

_____

_____

_____

4 **ANALYZING INDIVIDUALS** Why did David recognize the sin of another but not his own?

_____

_____

_____

_____

_____

_____

_____

_____

_____

_____

Isaiah's Message to the Israelites to Help the Hungry and the Poor

ESSENTIAL QUESTION
How does religion shape society?

DIRECTIONS: Read the following excerpt and answer the accompanying questions.

EXPLORE THE CONTEXT: This chapter of Isaiah is read in the synagogue on Yom Kippur (the Day of Atonement), the one day per year when people admit that they have sinned and seek God's forgiveness. They spend the day in prayer, trying to focus on being the good people that God wants them to be.

VOCABULARY

transgression: wrongdoing
forsook: turned away from, left
ordinance: law
wherefore: why
fast: to not eat

strife: trouble
smite: hit
afflicted: diseased or burdened
sabbath: day of the week set aside for rest and worship

PRIMARY SOURCE: BOOK

"58:1 Cry aloud, spare not, lift up thy voice like a trumpet, and show my people their transgression, and the house of Jacob their sins.

58:2 Yet they seek me daily, and delight to know my ways, as a nation that did righteousness, and forsook not the ordinance of their God: they ask of me the ordinances of justice; they take delight in approaching to God.

58:3 Wherefore have we fasted, say they, and thou seest not? wherefore have we afflicted our soul, and thou takest no knowledge? Behold, in the day of your fast ye find pleasure, and exact all your labours.

58:4 Behold, ye fast for strife and debate, and to smite with the fist of wickedness: ye shall not fast as ye do this day, to make your voice to be heard on high.

58:5 Is it such a fast that I have chosen? a day for a man to afflict his soul? is it to bow down his head as a bulrush, and to spread sackcloth and ashes under him? wilt thou call this a fast, and an acceptable day to the LORD?

58:6 Is not this the fast that I have chosen? to loose the bands of wickedness, to undo the heavy burdens, and to let the oppressed go free, and that ye break every yoke?

58:7 Is it not to deal thy bread to the hungry, and that thou bring the poor that are cast out to thy house? when thou seest the naked, that thou cover him; and that thou hide not thyself from thine own flesh?

58:8 Then shall thy light break forth as the morning, and thine health shall spring forth speedily: and thy righteousness shall go before thee; the glory of the LORD shall be thy reward.

58:9 Then shalt thou call, and the LORD shall answer; thou shalt cry, and he shall say, Here I am. If thou take away from the midst of thee the yoke, the putting forth of the finger, and speaking vanity;

58:10 And if thou draw out thy soul to the hungry, and satisfy the afflicted soul; then shall thy light rise in obscurity, and thy darkness be as the noon day:

58:11 And the LORD shall guide thee continually, and satisfy thy soul in drought, and make fat thy bones: and thou shalt be like a watered garden, and like a spring of water, whose waters fail not.

58:12 And they that shall be of thee shall build the old waste places: thou shalt raise up the foundations of many generations; and thou shalt be called, The repairer of the breach, The restorer of paths to dwell in.

58:13 If thou turn away thy foot from the sabbath, from doing thy pleasure on my holy day; and call the sabbath a delight, the holy of the LORD, honourable; and shalt honour him, not doing thine own ways, nor finding thine own pleasure, nor speaking thine own words:

58:14 Then shalt thou delight thyself in the LORD; and I will cause thee to ride upon the high places of the earth, and feed thee with the heritage of Jacob thy father: for the mouth of the LORD hath spoken it. "

—from the Hebrew Bible, Isaiah 58:1-14

1 **DETERMINING MEANING** How does this text explain the purpose of a fast?

_____

_____

_____

_____

_____

_____

2 **DETERMINING MEANING** What similes does the author of this document use to describe the changes in people after a fast? What do each of the similes mean?

_____

_____

_____

_____

_____

_____

_____

_____

_____

_____

_____

_____

_____

3 **DETERMINING CENTRAL IDEAS** What is the main idea of this passage?

_____

_____

_____

_____

_____

_____

_____

_____

_____

4 **COMPARING AND CONTRASTING** How is the main idea of this text similar to the main ideas expressed in the Ten Commandments?

_____

_____

_____

_____

_____

_____

_____

_____

ESSENTIAL QUESTION

How does religion shape society?

As you gather evidence to answer the Essential Question, think about:

- how the Israelites went from being led by kings to being led by temple priests and scribes.
- why the Torah serves as the center of a worship service.

My Notes

_____

_____

_____

_____

_____

_____

_____

_____

The Development of Judaism

DIRECTIONS: Search for evidence in Chapter 4, Lesson 3 to help you answer the following questions.

1 ANALYZING IDEAS How is the Hebrew Bible a multipurpose document for the Jewish people?

_____

_____

_____

_____

_____

2 INFERRING How does the account of the prophet Daniel demonstrate to Jews that God will rescue them from harm and that good will triumph over evil?

_____

_____

_____

_____

3 COMPARING AND CONTRASTING How is the biblical account of Daniel similar to other accounts of Israelites in crisis in the Hebrew Bible?

_____

_____

_____

_____

_____

4 **ANALYZING INDIVIDUALS** In the graphic organizer below, write the roles of each member of a Jewish family in the time of the ancient Israelites. Then describe how a person described in the Hebrew Bible is used to reinforce those roles in the family.

Roles of Ancient Israelite Family Members	Examples of Roles in the Hebrew Bible
Father	
Daughter	
Son	

5 **ANALYZING TEXT** In the graphic organizer below, choose two laws of Judaism described in the text that are still observed today. Then describe how they were observed by ancient Israelites.

Jewish Law Observed Today	How the Law Was Observed By Ancient Israelites

Copyright © McGraw-Hill Education; Maimonides, Moses. Translated 1904 by M. Friedlander. The Guide for the Perplexed, Second Edition. London: Routledge & Kegan Paul Ltd.

ESSENTIAL QUESTION
How does religion shape society?

Moses Maimonides on Jewish Dietary Laws

DIRECTIONS: Read the following excerpt and answer the accompanying questions.

EXPLORE THE CONTEXT: The dietary laws of the Jewish people are called kashrut. Moses Maimonides (my•MON•ih•deez), a twelfth-century scholar who was born in what is now Spain and completed his career in Egypt, wrote works of philosophy and Jewis law. In this excerpt, he interprets the laws regarding animals.

PRIMARY SOURCE: BOOK

❝It is prohibited to cut off a limb of a living animal and eat it, because such [an] act would produce cruelty, and develop it: besides, the heathen kings used to do it: it was also a kind of idolatrous worship to cut off a certain limb of a living animal and to eat it. . . . Since, therefore, the desire of procuring good food necessitates the slaying of animals, the Law enjoins that the death of the animal should be the easiest. It is not allowed to torment the animal by cutting the throat in a clumsy manner, by poleaxing, or by cutting off a limb whilst the animal is alive. . . . It is also prohibited to kill an animal with its young on the same day, in order that people should be restrained and prevented from killing the two together in such a manner that the young is slain in the sight of the mother; for the pain of the animals under such circumstances is very great. There is no difference in this case between the pain of man and the pain of other living beings. ❞

—from *Guide for the Perplexed* (1190)

VOCABULARY

kashrut: Jewish religious laws concerning food and diet

poleaxing: slaughtering with a battle-ax

prohibited: not allowed

slain: killed

circumstances: conditions; situation

1 DETERMINING MEANING What does Maimonides mean by "torment," and what activities in the document fall into that category of behavior?

_____

_____

_____

_____

2 CITING TEXT EVIDENCE What evidence in the text can you find for why it is not allowed in Jewish dietary laws to use meat from an animal that has had a limb cut off while it was still alive? How do each of these reasons help you understand the laws of kashrut?

_____

_____

_____

_____

3 INFERRING Based on this excerpt about Jewish dietary laws, what can you infer about how animals should be treated when they are being killed for food?

_____

_____

_____

_____

4 ANALYZING PERSPECTIVES How does this text reveal the Jewish perspective on similarities between animals and humans?

_____

_____

_____

_____

_____

Nehemiah and the Rebuilding of the Walls of Jerusalem

DIRECTIONS: Read the following excerpt and answer the accompanying questions.

EXPLORE THE CONTEXT: Nehemiah was authorized by the Persian king to rebuild the walls of Jerusalem. There was, however, strong opposition from the neighboring people, spearheaded by their leader Sanballat.

PRIMARY SOURCE: BOOK

" 33: But it came to pass that, when Sanballat heard that we built the wall, he was full of wrath, and took great indignation, and mocked the Jews.

34: And he spoke before his brethren and the army of Samaria, and said: 'What do these feeble Jews? will they restore at will? will they sacrifice? will they make an end this day? will they revive the stones out of the heaps of rubbish, seeing they are burned?'

35: Now Tobiah the Ammonite was by him, and he said: 'Even that which they build, if a fox go up, he shall break down their stone wall.'

36: Hear, O our G-d; for we are despised; and turn back their reproach upon their own head, and give them up to spoiling in a land of captivity;

37: and cover not their iniquity, and let not their sin be blotted out from before Thee; for they have vexed Thee before the builders.

38: So we built the wall; and all the wall was joined together unto half the height thereof; for the people had a mind to work. **"**

—from the Hebrew Bible, Nehemiah 3: 33-38

VOCABULARY

wrath: anger
indignation: offense
feeble: weak
reproach: disapproval
iniquity: morally wrong behavior
vexed: upset

Copyright © McGraw-Hill Education; Nelson, Larry. 1998. Based on 1917 translation of Jewish Publication Society Bible, Book of Nehemiah. Jewish Virtual Library - American-Israeli Cooperative Enterprise (AICE).

1 **DETERMINING MEANING** What does Tobiah mean by referring to the fox climbing the wall?

_____

_____

_____

_____

_____

2 **CITING TEXT EVIDENCE** What evidence can you find in the text that Jerusalem was extremely important to the Jews?

_____

_____

_____

_____

_____

3 **ANALYZING INDIVIDUALS** How did the Jews react to being mocked?

_____

_____

_____

4 **MAKING CONNECTIONS** How does this text reflect principles of Judaism found in the text about the Yom Kippur fast?

_____

_____

_____

_____

_____

_____

ESSENTIAL QUESTION

How does religion shape society?

As you gather evidence to answer the Essential Question, think about:

• the different reasons for translating the Hebrew Bible into Greek.

• the importance of the Dead Sea Scrolls to our understanding of the practice of Judaism.

My Notes

_____

_____

_____

_____

_____

_____

_____

The Jews in The Mediterranean World

DIRECTIONS: Search for evidence in Chapter 4, Lesson 4 to help you answer the following questions.

1 IDENTIFYING CAUSE AND EFFECT How did the Jewish-Roman wars lead to the diaspora?

_____

_____

_____

_____

_____

_____

2 ANALYZING IDEAS What role do rabbis and synagogues play in the preservation of the Jewish religion?

_____

_____

_____

_____

_____

_____

_____

3 DESCRIBING In the graphic organizer below, describe the different groups of Jews under Roman rule. Then describe the ways that each group practiced their religion.

Jewish Communities Under Roman Rule	Jewish Religious Practices
Sadducees	
Pharisees	
Essenes	
Zealots	

Mattathias and the King

ESSENTIAL QUESTION

How does religion shape society?

DIRECTIONS: Read the following excerpt and answer the accompanying questions.

EXPLORE THE CONTEXT: Mattathias (mah•tah•TYE•uhs) was an Israelite leader whose story is known as an example of the persistence of the Israelites' religious faith.

PRIMARY SOURCE: BOOK

VOCABULARY

renegade: traitors

Gentiles: non-Jewish people

covenant: agreement

profane: distasteful and wrong, against religious law

ordinances: laws

❝11 In those days [the reign of Antiochus Epiphanes] certain renegades came out from Israel and misled many, saying, "Let us go and make a covenant with the Gentiles around us, for since we separated from them many disasters have come upon us." 12 This proposal pleased them, 13 and some of the people eagerly went to the king, who authorized them to observe the ordinances of the Gentiles. 14 So they built a gymnasium in Jerusalem, according to Gentile custom, 15 and removed the marks of circumcision, and abandoned the holy covenant. . . .

41 Then the king wrote to his whole kingdom that all should be one people, 42 and that all should give up their particular customs. 43 All the Gentiles accepted the command of the king. Many even from Israel gladly adopted his religion; they sacrificed to idols and profaned the sabbath. 44 And the king sent letters by messengers to Jerusalem and the towns of Judah; he directed them to follow customs strange to the land, 45 to forbid burnt offerings and sacrifices and drink offerings in the sanctuary, to profane sabbaths and festivals, 46 to defile the sanctuary and the priests, 47 to build altars and sacred precincts and shrines for idols, to sacrifice swine and other unclean animals, 48 and to leave their sons uncircumcised. They were to make themselves abominable by everything unclean

and profane, 49 so that they would forget the law and change all the ordinances. 50 He added,[e] "And whoever does not obey the command of the king shall die.". . .

62 But many in Israel stood firm and were resolved in their hearts not to eat unclean food. 63 They chose to die rather than to be defiled by food or to profane the holy covenant; and they dld die. 64 Very great wrath came upon Israel. . . .

9 But Mattathias answered and said in a loud voice: "Even if all the nations that live under the rule of the king obey him, and have chosen to obey his commandments, every one of them abandoning the religion of their ancestors, 20 I and my sons and my brothers will continue to live by the covenant of our ancestors. 21 Far be it from us to desert the law and the ordinances. 22 We will not obey the king's words by turning aside from our religion to the right hand or to the left. **99**

—from the Hebrew Bible, I Maccabees 1: 11-15, 41-50, 62-64; 2: 5, 20-22

1 **DETERMINING MEANING** Based on your reading of the text, what do you think the writer of this document mean by the "holy covenant"?

_____

_____

_____

_____

_____

2 **DESCRIBING** How does this document describe the notion of "unclean"?

_____

_____

_____

_____

_____

_____

_____

_____

_____

_____

_____

_____

3 CITING TEXT EVIDENCE What evidence in the text can you find for how Mattathias feels about the laws of his religion and the role they play in his life?

_____

_____

_____

_____

_____

_____

_____

4 ANALYZING How do Mattathias's actions reflect the historical precedent of keeping the faith? Who in past stories of the Israelites has a similar reaction to this type of challenge?

_____

_____

_____

_____

_____

_____

_____

Capital Cases

ESSENTIAL QUESTION
How does religion shape society?

DIRECTIONS: Read the following excerpt and answer the accompanying questions.

EXPLORE THE CONTEXT: The following excerpt is a discussion of Jewish law.

PRIMARY SOURCE: BOOK

66 How were witnesses admonished in capital cases? They were brought in, and admonished to the effect that 'what you say may be merely your own opinion, or hearsay, or secondhand, or derived from a trustworthy person. Perhaps you do not know that we intend to question you by examination and inquiry. Know, moreover, that capital cases are not like non-capital cases: in non-capital cases a man may pay money and so make expiation; but in capital cases the blood of the accused and of his posterity may cling to him (the witness) to the end of the world. For so we find it in the case of Cain, who slew his brother, as it is written: THE VOICE OF THE BLOODS OF THY BROTHER CRIES TO ME FROM THE GROUND; —not the blood of thy brother, but the bloods of thy brother—his blood and that of his posterity.'

For this reason man was created one and alone in the world: to teach that whosoever destroys a single soul is regarded as though he destroyed a complete world, and whosoever saves a single soul is regarded as though he saved a complete world; and for the sake of peace among created beings that one man should not say to another, "My father was greater than thine," and that heretics should not say, "There are many ruling powers in heaven "; also to proclaim the greatness of the King of kings of kings, blessed be He! for mankind stamps a hundred coins with one seal, and they are all alike, but the King of kings of kings, blessed be He! has stamped every man with the seal of the first Adam, and not one of them is like his fellow. 1 So every single person is forced to say, The world was created for my sake. 99

—from Mishnah Sanhedrin 4:5, c. 200s C.E.

VOCABULARY

admonished: warned

hearsay: evidence that has no concrete proof, heard from someone else

expiation: the act of repaying for wrongdoing

posterity: future generations

1 **DETERMINING MEANING** What does the writer mean by "the blood of the accused and of his posterity may cling to him. . . ."? What does the writer mean by "his posterity"?

_____

_____

2 **INFERRING** The writer makes a distinction between capital and non-capital cases. What is the difference between the two kinds of cases?

_____

_____

3 **ANALYZING** Why does the murder of one person, from this writer's perspective, equal the murder of an entire world?

_____

_____

_____

_____

_____

4 **MAKING CONNECTIONS** How are this document and the document on Jewish dietary laws similar regarding the views of Judaism on the taking of a life? How do these similarities help you understand the Jewish perspective on the power of human beings to take lives or refrain from taking them?

_____

_____

_____

_____

_____

_____

ESSENTIAL QUESTION

How does religion shape society?

① Think About It

Review the supporting questions that you developed at the beginning of the chapter. Review the evidence that you gathered in Chapter 4. Were you able to answer each Supporting Question?

If there was not enough evidence to answer your Supporting Questions, what additional evidence do you think you need to consider?

_____

_____

_____

② Organize Your Evidence

Use a chart like the one below to organize the evidence you will use to support your Position Statement.

Source of Information	Specific evidence from the source to cite	How does the evidence support my Position Statement?	How does this evidence connect to modern life?

3 Write About It

A position statement related to the Essential Question should reflect your conclusion about the evidence. Write a Position Statement for the ESSENTIAL QUESTION: *How does religion shape society?*

_____

_____

_____

_____

_____

_____

_____

4 Talk About It

Work in a small group to present your position statement and evidence. Gather feedback from your classmates before you write your final conclusion. You may choose to refine your Position Statement after you have discussed it with your classmates. Group members should listen to one another's arguments, ask questions, and offer constructive advice to help each other create clear Position Statements.

_____

_____

_____

5 Connect to the Essential Question

On a separate piece of paper, develop an interview with an ancient Israelite person who is your age to answer the ESSENTIAL QUESTION: *How does religion shape society?*

CITIZENSHIP
TAKING ACTION

MAKE CONNECTIONS Jews throughout history have faced discrimination and persecution. Hostility or prejudice against Jews is called anti-Semitism. Hostility towards Jewish people reached its height in Europe before and during World War II, when Jews were murdered by the Nazis in the Holocaust. The Nazis were defeated, but anti-Semitism continues, even in the United States. Hate groups sometimes target Jews and Jewish organizations with violent acts. American Jews can face discrimination in employment and other parts of society.

DIRECTIONS: The Anti-Defamation League (ADL) was founded in the United States to fight anti-Semitism. Use the Internet to find the nearest office of the ADL in your state or region. Find out what steps the ADL recommends for schools and communities to take action against anti-Semitism. Then discuss as a class what actions would be effective in responding to anti-Semitic incidents among students and in the wider society.

_____

_____

_____

_____

_____

_____

_____

_____

_____

The Ancient Greeks

ESSENTIAL QUESTION

Why does conflict develop?

Think about how this question might relate to the Ancient Greek civilization.

TALK ABOUT IT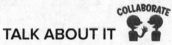

Discuss with a partner what information you would need in order to answer this question. For example, one question might be: Did the geography of Greece affect the development of conflict within its civilization?

DIRECTIONS: Write down three more questions that might help you explain the influence of conflict as the Greeks developed as a civilization.

MY RESEARCH QUESTIONS

Supporting Question 1:

_____

_____

Supporting Question 2:

_____

_____

Supporting Question 3:

_____

_____

Rise of Greek Civilization

DIRECTIONS: Search for evidence in Chapter 5, Lesson 1 to help you answer the following questions.

ESSENTIAL QUESTION

Why does conflict develop?

As you gather evidence to answer the Essential Question, think about:

- the distance between the communities in Greece.
- reasons for the Dark Age and the later recovery of Greece.

1 ANALYZING What problems or benefits did the people of ancient Greece experience as a result of being surrounded by seas and mountains?

_____

_____

_____

_____

_____

2 COMPARING AND CONTRASTING In what ways were the Mycenaeans and Minoans alike and different?

My Notes

_____

_____

_____

_____

_____

_____

_____

_____

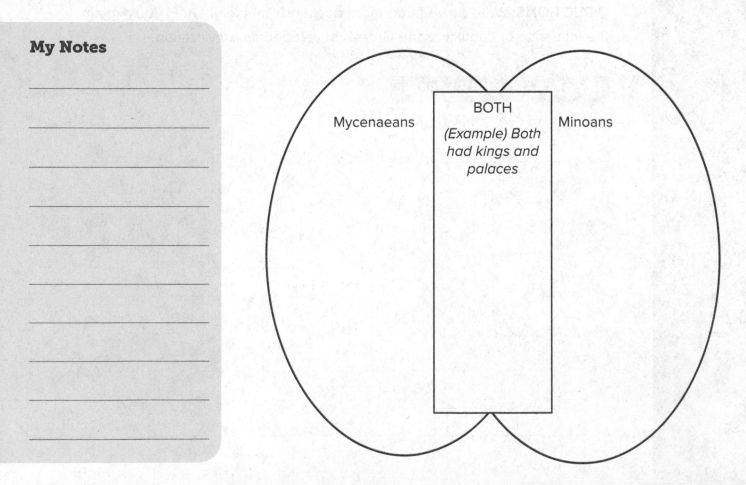

Mycenaeans   BOTH   Minoans

(Example) Both had kings and palaces

3 **IDENTIFYING CAUSE AND EFFECT** Fill in the chart below to show the relationship between the fall of the Mycenaeans and its effects during the Dark Age. Use details to fill in what the effects were for each event listed.

Fall of Mycenaeans	

Dorians invaded mainland	

Many people left the mainland to escape	

4 **HISTORY** What were the historic developments in the restoration of Greece? Fill in the web with details of Greek accomplishments after the Dark Age.

The Rise of Greece

Chariot Race

DIRECTIONS: Study the following image and answer the accompanying questions.

EXPLORE THE CONTEXT: This photo of a vase created around 500 B.C.E. to 480 B.C.E. includes an image of a chariot. Chariots had a great impact on ancient Greek Civilization.

PRIMARY SOURCE: IMAGE

1A COMPARING Compare the image of the chariot and its driver with the picture of the Greek city-state hoplites in Lesson 1. Describe any advantages or disadvantages of fighting in a chariot as compared with being a heavily armed hoplite.

_____

_____

_____

_____

_____

1B **ANALYZING** How did the use of chariots contribute to the development of conflict?

_____

_____

_____

_____

2 **HISTORY** Why would chariot racing have become a sporting event when the chariots were designed for war?

_____

_____

_____

3 **DRAWING CONCLUSIONS** By examining the image, can you determine how the nobles controlled their horses? Why would control be important? Support your opinion with reasons.

_____

_____

_____

_____

_____

4 **ANALYZING POINT OF VIEW** Whose point of view, the hoplites or the nobles, is illustrated in the image? Why do you think this image would have been painted onto vases and walls of palaces? What evidence can you supply from Lesson 1 to support your answer?

_____

_____

_____

_____

_____

_____

Hesiod on Conflict

ESSENTIAL QUESTION

Why does conflict develop?

DIRECTIONS: Read the following excerpt and answer the accompanying questions.

EXPLORE THE CONTEXT: The excerpt from *The Ancient Olympics*, by Nigel Spivey, provides insight from poetry written by Hesiod, an early Greek writer.

VOCABULARY

strife: quarrel, conflict
supernatural: something related to a God or Deity
reckoned with: dealt with
malevolent: having an evil influence

exulting: rejoicing, feeling joy or happiness
mortals: humans
emulation: imitation of something admired
vied: competed for superiority

SECONDARY SOURCE: BOOK

“ It was one of the earliest surviving Greek poets, Hesiod, composing his verses probably around 700 BC, who not only made 'Strife' (Eris) a supernatural force to be reckoned with, but also divided this force into one Strife that was useful and productive (Eris agathos) and another that caused nothing but grief for humankind. This malevolent Strife, 'exulting in bad things' (kakochartos), was the bringer of war and dissent to the world. Good Strife . . . encouraged mortals to make the most of their brief time on earth; Bad Strife sets up lusts for battle and bloodshed. Good Strife nurtured desires for wealth and fame; Bad Strife was a destroyer of lives and property. Good Strife urged creative industry, stirring the energies of emulation. So craftsmen competed amongst themselves, so farmers toiled to get the best from their land, so even beggars vied in their begging, and poets challenged other poets. ”

— Nigel Spivey, *The Ancient Olympics: A History,* 2004 C.E.

1 **DETERMINING MEANING** Spivey explains the importance of *Strife*, according to Hesiod. Examine the meaning of the word *strife* as it is usually defined today. How does that compare with Hesiod's point of view concerning *Strife*? Explain.

_____

_____

_____

2 **CITING TEXT EVIDENCE** Which phrases or lines from Hesiod would relate to the Olympics, both then and now?

_____

_____

_____

_____

_____

3 **EXPLAINING EFFECTS** Review Lesson 1 to see how Greek citizens viewed their individual city-states. Describe the effects of "good strife" in the individual polis and the effects of "bad strife" among the city-states of Greece.

_____

_____

_____

_____

_____

_____

4 **DRAWING CONCLUSIONS** What character qualities would a person choosing Hesiod's "good strife" exhibit? Explain.

_____

_____

_____

_____

5 **RELATING EVENTS** If you faced a competition at school and felt you were not ready, what ideas could you apply from Hesiod's poetry theme?

_____

_____

_____

_____

ESSENTIAL QUESTION

Why does conflict develop?

As you gather evidence to answer the Essential Question, think about:

- the resentment people had toward the control of the wealthy nobles.
- the reign of controlling tyrants before the rise of oligarchies and democracies.

My Notes

_____

_____

_____

_____

_____

_____

_____

_____

Sparta and Athens: City-State Rivals

DIRECTIONS: Search for evidence in Chapter 5, Lesson 2 to help you answer the following questions.

1 **DETERMINING SUPPORTING DETAILS** Complete the chart to define and compare the differences in the following types of government.

Government

The way actions are controlled by laws or force.

Oligarchy

Democracy

Tyranny

2 ECONOMICS How might Sparta's culture affect its relationships with other city-states?

_____

_____

_____

3 INFERRING In the graphic organizer below, list ways Spartan men and women were raised and the roles each played in Sparta. Then make an inference about what kind of city-state Sparta was.

Spartan Men	Spartan Women
1.	1.
2.	2.
3.	3.

4 EXPLAINING CAUSE AND EFFECT How did debt and slavery cause reform in the city-state of Athens? List a chain of effects that resulted from this reform.

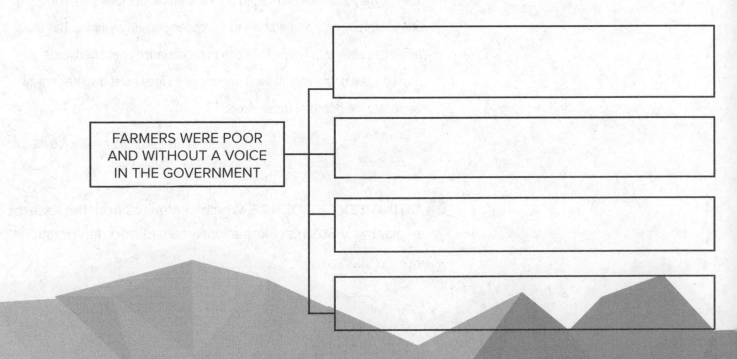

FARMERS WERE POOR AND WITHOUT A VOICE IN THE GOVERNMENT

Democratic Reforms

Copyright © McGraw-Hill Education; Plutarch; Plutarch; Translated 1914 by Bernadotte Perrin. Plutarch's Lives, Volume 1. Cambridge, Massachusetts: Harvard University Press; London: William Heinemann Ltd.

ESSENTIAL QUESTION

Why does conflict develop?

DIRECTIONS: Study the following excerpt and answer the accompanying questions.

EXPLORE THE CONTEXT: Plutarch was a Greek biographer and essayist whose excerpt describes reforms put in place by Solon.

PRIMARY SOURCE: BOOK

" [W]ishing to leave all the magistracies in the hands of the well-to-do, as they were, but to give the common people a share in the rest of the government, of which they had hitherto [so far] been deprived, Solon made an appraisement of the property of the citizens. Those who enjoyed a yearly increase of five hundred measures (wet and dry), he placed in the first class, and called them Pentakosiomedimnoi; the second class was composed of those who were able to keep a horse, or had a yearly increase of three hundred measures, and they were called Hippada Telountes, since they paid a Knight's tax; the members of the third class, whose yearly increase amounted to two hundred measures (wet and dry together), were called Zeugitai. All the rest were called Thetes; they were not allowed to hold any office, but took part in the administration only as members of the assembly and as jurors. This last privilege seemed at first of no moment [importance], but afterwards proved to be of the very highest importance, since most disputes finally came into the hands of these jurors. "

—from *Plutarch's Lives,* c. 96-98 C.E.

VOCABULARY

magistracies: control of territory

appraisement: a statement of the value of something

measures: a standard unit used to measure quantity

administration: the people who manage the government

disputes: an argument or difference of opinion

deprived: lacking something considered necessary

1 **CITING TEXT EVIDENCE** Which sentences from the excerpt explain why Solon's reforms were considered democratic?

_____

_____

_____

_____

_____

_____

2 COMPARING AND CONTRASTING Compare and contrast Plutarch's description of democratic reforms with the text in Lesson 2.

_____

_____

_____

_____

_____

_____

3 DETERMINING POINT OF VIEW Discuss with a partner what you think Plutarch believes about Solon's ideas of governing. What does Plutarch suggest by the word choices in this sentence: "to give the common people a share in the rest of the government, of which they had hitherto [so far] been deprived." Why might he have chosen the word _deprived_?

_____

_____

_____

_____

_____

_____

4 DRAWING CONCLUSIONS From reading the excerpt, how do you think the people responded to Solon's reforms? Compare your conclusion with the explanation in Lesson 2.

_____

_____

_____

_____

Spartan Sayings

ESSENTIAL QUESTION

Why does conflict develop?

VOCABULARY

ventured: took a risk to go out and do something
valour: courage, bravery

memorial: a time or event set aside to remember
oration: speech
vanquished: conquered

1 INFERRING What character traits were most valued by the Spartans and how did these traits affect their culture? Use evidence from the excerpts to support your ideas.

_____

_____

_____

_____

_____

_____

_____

_____

_____

_____

DIRECTIONS: Study the following excerpt and answer the accompanying questions.

EXPLORE THE CONTEXT: Plutarch, the Greek writer, also collected quotations from the people of Sparta. These quotes will help explain the ideas and attitudes of the citizens of ancient Sparta.

PRIMARY SOURCE: BOOK

"ANAXANDRIDAS

When another person asked why the Spartans, in their wars, ventured boldly into danger, he said, 'Because we train ourselves to have regard for life and not, like others, to be timid about it.'

ANDROCLEIDAS

Androcleidas the Spartan, who had a crippled leg, enrolled himself among the fighting-men. And when some persons were insistent that he be not accepted because he was crippled, he said, 'But I do not have to run away, but to stay where I am when I fight the opposing foe.'

ARISTON

1 When someone inquired how many Spartans there were in all, he said, 'Enough to keep away our enemies.'

2 When one of the Athenians read a memorial oration in praise of those who fell at the hands of the Spartans, he said, 'What kind of men, then, do you think ours must be who vanquished these?'

ZEUXIDAMUS

3 When someone inquired why they kept the laws in regard to bravery unwritten, and did not have them written down and thus give them to the young men to read, Zeuxidamus said, 'Because the young ought to accustom themselves to deeds of manly valour, a better thing than to apply their mind to writings.'**"**

— Plutarch, *Apophthegmata Laconica*, c. 96-98 C.E.

2 CITING TEXT EVIDENCE Discuss with a partner the tough mindset that was characteristic of the Spartans. Use evidence from the quotations to support your answer.

_____

_____

_____

_____

_____

3 CONTRASTING How do the Spartan values stated in the quotations contrast with the values of Athenians described in Lesson 2?

_____

_____

_____

_____

4 DRAWING CONCLUSIONS What do the quotations suggest about the military strength of ancient Sparta? Support your answer with details.

_____

_____

_____

5 CIVICS Imagine that our nation passed laws that schools would no longer teach reading but, instead, focus solely on building physical strength. How do you think our society would change? Explain.

_____

_____

_____

_____

Greece and Persia

DIRECTIONS: Search for evidence in Chapter 5, Lesson 3 to help you answer the following questions.

ESSENTIAL QUESTION

Why does conflict develop?

As you gather evidence to answer the Essential Question, think about:

- how Persia's great King Cyrus built a growing empire.
- the clash between Greece and Persia as the Persians tried to move into Europe.

My Notes

_____

_____

_____

_____

_____

_____

_____

_____

1 **CITING TEXT EVIDENCE** How is Persia's king, Cyrus, described? Fill in the chart below with factual evidence from the text.

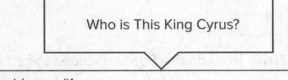

Who is This King Cyrus?

Text evidence #1:

Text evidence #2:

Text evidence #3:

2 **SEQUENCING** Identify the events in the expansion of the Persian Empire after Cyrus. Write the events in the organizer according to the historical sequence.

Sequence of Events in the Expansion of the Persian Empire
1
2
3
4
5
6

3 **IDENTIFYING CAUSE AND EFFECT** In the graphic organizer below, describe how the Greeks responded to each advance by the Persians.

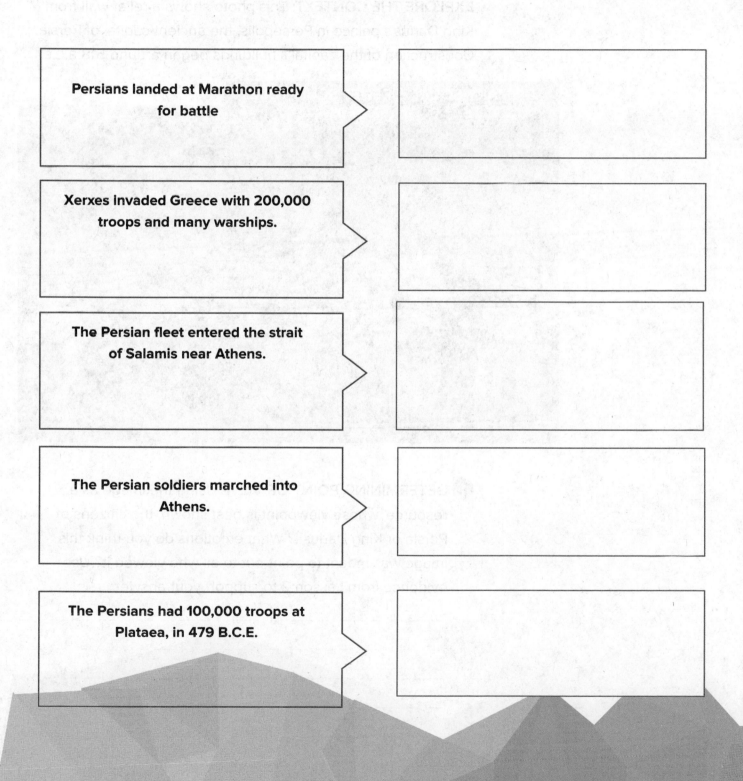

Persians landed at Marathon ready for battle

Xerxes invaded Greece with 200,000 troops and many warships.

The Persian fleet entered the strait of Salamis near Athens.

The Persian soldiers marched into Athens.

The Persians had 100,000 troops at Plataea, in 479 B.C.E.

ESSENTIAL QUESTION

Why does conflict develop?

King Darius

DIRECTIONS: Study the following image of King Darius I of Persia and answer the accompanying questions.

EXPLORE THE CONTEXT: This photo shows a relief wall from King Darius's palace in Persepolis, the ancient capital of Persia. Construction of the capital's buildings began around 518 B.C.E.

PRIMARY SOURCE: RELIEF SCULPTURE

 DETERMINING POINT OF VIEW Using the image as a resource, whose viewpoint is best shown, the citizens of Persia or King Darius I? What emotions do you think this image was meant to point out to all who viewed it? Use evidence from Lesson 2 to support your answer.

_____

_____

_____

_____

_____

_____

2 **DRAWING CONCLUSIONS** What role does Zoroastrianism play in how King Darius I is depicted in the image? Reread the description in your text and decide if it corresponds with the image shown. Explain.

_____

_____

_____

_____

_____

_____

3 **COMPARING AND CONTRASTING** What does the image suggest about the authority of kings of Persia? How did the rule of Persian kings contrast with the Greek form of government? How are both systems similar?

_____

_____

_____

_____

_____

4 **DRAWING CONCLUSIONS** What does King Darius I's image suggest to you about the reason for conflict between Persia and Greece?

_____

_____

_____

_____

_____

Copyright © McGraw-Hill Education; Abbott, Jacob. 1902. Makers of History - Xerxes. New York and London: Harper & Brothers Publishers.

The Defeat of Xerxes at the Battle of Salamis

ESSENTIAL QUESTION
Why does conflict develop?

DIRECTIONS: Study the following excerpt and answer the accompanying questions.

EXPLORE THE CONTEXT: Artemisia was a courageous Greek woman who had married King Halicarnassus in 500 B.C.E. After he died, she accepted her role as Queen. She became loyal to Persia and made herself famous by becoming a naval commander.

SECONDARY SOURCE: BOOK

66 He said that he would consult some of the other commanders upon the subject. He did so, and then, before coming to a final decision, he determined to confer with Artemisia. He remembered that she had counseled him not to attack the Greeks at Salamis, and, as the result had proved that counsel to be eminently wise, he felt the greater confidence in asking her judgment again. He accordingly sent for Artemisia, and, directing all the officers, as well as his own attendants, to retire, he held a private consultation with her in respect to his plans.

'Mardonius proposes,' said he, 'that the expedition should on no account be abandoned in consequence of this disaster, for he says that the fleet is a very unimportant part of our force, and that the army still remains unharmed. He proposes that, if I should decide myself to return to Persia, I should leave three hundred thousand men with him, and he undertakes, if I will do so, to complete, with them, the subjugation of Greece. Tell me what you think of this plan. You evinced so much sagacity in foreseeing the result of this engagement at Salamis, that I particularly wish to know your opinion.' 99

— Jacob Abbott, *Makers of History: Xerxes,* 1878 C.E.

VOCABULARY:

confer: to seek someone else's opinion

eminently: exceptionally

consultation: a meeting to gather another's ideas

expedition: a journey or trip

undertakes: begins

subjugation: defeat

evinced: demonstrated

sagacity: wisdom

1 **ANALYZING** Which words describing Artemisia show how much Xerxes admired her?

_____

_____

2 **DRAWING CONCLUSIONS** Using information about Salamis in Lesson 3, why do you think Artemisia counseled Xerxes not to attack there?

_____

_____

_____

_____

_____

3 HISTORY Discuss with a partner what you can infer about the role of females in this time period. What is the author suggesting about Artemisia in this passage when Xerxes calls her for a consultation?

_____

_____

_____

4 **INFERRING** Why do you think Xerxes wanted a private consultation with Artemisia about the possibility of a future battle with the Greeks?

_____

_____

_____

5 **IDENTIFYING CONNECTIONS** If you had an important decision to make, who would you consult? Would you go to a trusted friend or to someone you knew had experience in the area of concern?

_____

_____

_____

Glory, War, and Decline

DIRECTIONS: Search for evidence in Chapter 5, Lesson 4 to help you answer the following questions.

1 **IDENTIFYING CAUSES** Use the chart to record important details that resulted from the leadership of Pericles in Athens.

ESSENTIAL QUESTION

Why does conflict develop?

As you gather evidence to answer the Essential Question, think about

- how the economic and political strength of Athens gave them more influence.

- how Sparta became the head of an alliance of city-states to rival Athens.

Athens Under the Leadership of Pericles

PERICLES

My Notes

_____

_____

_____

_____

_____

_____

_____

_____

2 **HISTORY** If Athens prospered under the leadership of Pericles, what went wrong? What was the trigger, or initial cause, of conflict?

_____

_____

_____

_____

_____

_____

3 ANALYZING What were the democratic principles encouraged in the famous speech, now known as Pericles's Funeral Oration?

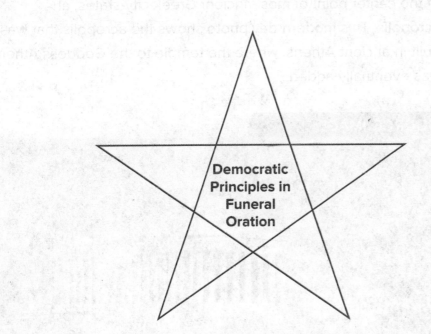

Democratic
Principles in
Funeral
Oration

4 IDENTIFYING CAUSES Use the chart below to record events that caused Athens to finally lose the Peloponnesian War.

Causes of the Surrender Of Athens

The Acropolis

DIRECTIONS: Study the following image and answer the accompanying questions.

EXPLORE THE CONTEXT: This image depicts a famous example of the center point of most ancient Greek city-states, an acropolis. This modern-day photo shows the acropolis that was built in ancient Athens, where the temple to the Goddess Athena was eventually added.

PRIMARY SOURCE: IMAGE

1A **DESCRIBING** Describe the famous Acropolis as seen in this image.

_____

_____

1B **IDENTIFYING CONNECTIONS** Describe the features of the Acropolis that have been used in more modern architecture. Describe any important buildings you may know of in America using those ancient Greek features.

_____

_____

_____

2 **ANALYZING** How was the Acropolis protected?

_____

_____

3 **DRAWING CONCLUSIONS** Does this image of the Athenian Acropolis correspond to the description of Greek acropolis structures in Lesson 1? Explain.

_____

_____

_____

4 **CITING TEXT EVIDENCE** In Lesson 4, reread about the days after the Persian Wars and Pericles. Why did the Athenian victory and leadership of Pericles contribute to the building of additional monuments at the Acropolis?

_____

_____

_____

_____

The Plague in Athens

ESSENTIAL QUESTION

Why does conflict develop?

DIRECTIONS: Study the following excerpt and answer the accompanying questions.

EXPLORE THE CONTEXT: Thucydides, another well-known historian from Ancient Greece, wrote about the war between Athens and Sparta. The war was called the Peloponnesian War because of Sparta's location in the Peloponnesus, a peninsula in southern Greece. In addition to the problems of war, Athens was struck by an epidemic, killing many Athenians, including the leader Pericles. Attica is the region around and including Athens.

VOCABULARY

thence: from there

thither: onward in a new direction

lazar-house: a place where people with leprosy were confined

epidemic: a rapid spread of disease

scourge: suffering, calamity

copious: plentiful, a large amount

draughts: cups

oblivion: forgetting or not knowing

PRIMARY SOURCE: BOOK

❝At the beginning of the next summer the Peloponnesians again entered Attica, and resumed their work of devastation, destroying the young crops, and wrecking whatever had been spared in the previous year. Before they had been many days in Attica, a new and far more terrible visitation came upon the Athenians, threatening them with total extinction as a people. We have seen how the whole upper city, with the space between the Long Walls, and the harbour-town of Peiraeus, was packed with a vast multitude of human beings, penned together, like sheep in a fold. Into these huddled masses now crept a subtle and unseen foe, striking down his victims by hundreds and by thousands. That foe was the Plague, which beginning in Southern Africa, and descending thence to Egypt, reached the southern shores of the Mediterranean, and passed on to Peiraeus, having been carried thither by seamen who trafficked between northern Africa and Greece. . . .

From the description of the symptoms we may conclude that this epidemic was similar to that dreadful scourge of mankind which has been almost conquered by modern science, the small-pox. The patient who had taken the infection was first attacked in the head, with inflammation of the eyes, and violent headache. By degrees the poison worked its way into the whole system, . . . One of the most distressing features of the

disease was a raging thirst, which could not be appeased by the most copious draughts of water; and the internal heat, which produced this effect, caused also a frightful irritability of the skin, so that the sufferer could not bear the touch of the lightest and most airy fabrics, . . . Of those who recovered, many bore the marks of the sickness to their graves, by the loss of a hand, a foot, or an eye; while others were affected in their minds, remaining in blank oblivion, without power to recognise themselves or their friends."

— from *Stories from Thucydides*, c. 400s B.C.E.

1 **ANALYZING SOURCES** In the first two sentences, what emotions do you think the author wanted the reader to feel? What evidence can you provide to support your answer?

_____

_____

_____

_____

_____

_____

_____

_____

2 **COMPARING AND CONTRASTING** In Lesson 4, the city-state of Athens is described at its height after the Persian Wars. What words would best describe Athens then? Compare and contrast this condition to that of Athens at the time of the writing by Thucydides.

_____

_____

_____

_____

_____

_____

_____

_____

3 SUMMARIZING Describe the impact of the plague on the people of Athens and why it would have affected the outcome of the war with Sparta.

_____

_____

_____

_____

_____

_____

_____

4 CITING TEXT EVIDENCE How does the author Thucydides elaborate the main idea that Athens was destroyed during the Peloponnesian War? Use evidence from the excerpt to support your ideas.

_____

_____

_____

_____

_____

_____

_____

_____

ESSENTIAL QUESTION
Why does conflict develop?

1 Think About It

Review the supporting questions you developed at the opening of the chapter. Review the evidence you found in Chapter 5. Were you able to answer each of your Supporting Questions?

If you didn't find enough evidence to answer your Supporting Questions, what do you think you need to consider?

_____

_____

_____

_____

2 Organize Your Evidence

Use a chart like the one below to organize the evidence you will need to support your Position Statement.

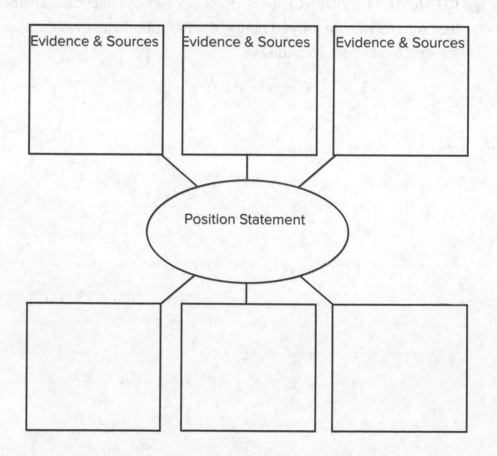

Evidence & Sources   Evidence & Sources   Evidence & Sources

Position Statement

Talk About It

In a small group or with a partner, discuss your position statement and the evidence you have gathered. Check your group's understanding of your evidence and respond to questions your members may have while considering their input.

4 Connect to the Essential Question

On a separate piece of paper, write a decree, or instruction, to your citizens as if you were an important leader in ancient Athens. What wisdom would you pass onto the people in a young democracy? Be sure to address the answers to the ESSENTIAL QUESTION: *Why does conflict develop?* What advice could you give your followers that would help them live peacefully, using what you've learned about conflict?

CITIZENSHIP
TAKING ACTION

MAKE CONNECTIONS: Many kings and city-state leaders fought to gain land and power in the days of ancient Greece. Though we have not experienced a foreign power attempting to gain territory *within* America today, some world leaders still seek dominion over other countries. One place that was recently overtaken by Russia was the Crimea region of Ukraine. Many members of the international community of nations placed sanctions (penalties, often with trade agreements) on Russia for their invasion. However, Russia continues to occupy the region militarily.

DIRECTIONS: Research the causes of this specific conflict. Determine if the events that caused Russia to act aggressively are similar to reasons you discovered for conflicts among Greeks and Persians.

Write a speech that you could present to the United Nations to promote an international agreement to turn around Russia's invasion in Ukraine.

_____

_____

_____

_____

_____

_____

_____

_____

_____

_____

_____

_____

CHAPTER 6

Greek Civilization

ESSENTIAL QUESTION

What makes a culture unique?

Think about how this question might relate to the culture of ancient Greece.

TALK ABOUT IT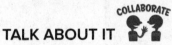

Discuss with a partner what type of information you would need to know to answer this question. For example, one question might be: What kind of cultural advancements happened in ancient Greece?

DIRECTIONS: Now write down three additional questions that would help you explain the parts of society that makes a culture unique.

MY RESEARCH QUESTIONS

Supporting Question 1:

_____

_____

Supporting Question 2:

_____

_____

Supporting Question 3:

_____

_____

ESSENTIAL QUESTION

What makes a culture unique?

As you gather evidence to answer the Essential Question, think about:

- the religion adopted by people in ancient Greece.
- how theater and literature influenced the thought of ancient Greek communities.

My Notes

_____

_____

_____

_____

_____

_____

_____

_____

_____

Greek Culture

DIRECTIONS: Search for evidence in Chapter 6, Lesson 1 to help you answer the following questions.

1 **SUMMARIZING** Use the chart below to make notes about the religious beliefs and practices of ancient Greece.

Religious Beliefs	Religious Practices

2 **SUMMARIZING** Ancient Greek drama and literature remain parts of western culture today. As you reread the chapter, fill out the KWL chart below to record what you know, what you learned, and what you would like to learn about ancient Greek literature and drama.

Know	Want to Learn	Learned

3 ANALYZING Reread the section of the chapter about ancient Greek comedies and tragedies. Now think about the movies, plays, and stories you know of today. Write the name of one tragedy and one comedy that you have seen on television, in a theater, or read in literature.

_____

_____

_____

_____

_____

_____

_____

_____

_____

4 Look at the drawing of the Parthenon. What does the architecture tell you about the people who used it?

_____

_____

_____

_____

_____

_____

_____

_____

_____

_____

Greek Papyrus

DIRECTIONS: Examine the image below and answer the accompanying questions.

EXPLORE THE CONTEXT: This artifact from around the 300s B.C.E., which describes the battle of Salamis, is made of a plant material called papyrus. Papyrus grows best in wet areas of warm climates, like along the Nile River or in Mediterranean locations like Greece. This material was used as paper by early cultures. The ancient Greek people used papyrus to record their laws, poetry, and stories. Some papyrus artifacts have been recovered from graves. Others have been found wrapped and placed alongside mummies. Today, papyrus artifacts are preserved carefully in museums. They help modern historians understand what life was like many years ago.

PRIMARY SOURCE: ARTIFACT

1 GEOGRAPHY   What can you tell about the climate and environment of ancient Greece from the artifact?

_____

_____

_____

2 HISTORICAL CONTEXT   What type of document is pictured in this image? How does this help you understand ancient Greek culture?

_____

_____

_____

3 HISTORICAL INFERENCE   The writing on the papyrus tells the story of an important battle in which a Greek fleet overpowered Persian naval forces that were much greater In number. What inference can you make about how documents such as this were shared among people in ancient Greece?

_____

_____

_____

4 DRAWING CONCLUSIONS   What conclusion can you draw about the artifact from knowing that it has been preserved from ancient times?

_____

_____

_____

The Temple of Apollo at Delphi

DIRECTIONS: Look at the image and answer the accompanying questions.

EXPLORE THE CONTEXT: The image shows the ruins of the Temple of Apollo at Delphi. The temple was built around the 700s B.C.E. Temples were often dedicated to specific Gods and Goddesses, especially Apollo, the God of the sun. The grand temple was home to the Oracle of Delphi and would have been considered a sacred site. Today it draws thousands of visitors who want to understand the culture of people who lived long ago.

PRIMARY SOURCE: ARCHITECTURE

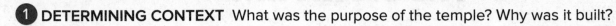

1 DETERMINING CONTEXT What was the purpose of the temple? Why was it built?

_____

_____

_____

_____

2 ANALYZING What can you tell about the number of people who likely visited the temple when it was built? What type of people likely visited the temple? What evidence can you gather from the image that helps you answer that question?

_____

_____

_____

_____

_____

_____

_____

3 GEOGRAPHY What features of the setting of the temple of Apollo at Delphi help you understand its meaning and importance?

_____

_____

_____

4 ECONOMICS What could you learn about the culture of ancient Greece from visiting the ruins of the temple of Apollo at Delphi?

_____

_____

_____

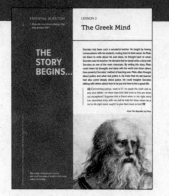

The Greek Mind

DIRECTIONS: Search for evidence in Chapter 6, Lesson 2 to help you answer the following question.

ESSENTIAL QUESTION

What makes a culture unique?

As you gather evidence to answer the Essential Question, think about:

- the thinkers that shaped ancient Greek philosophy.

- how people use facts and beliefs to build ideas about science.

- how our own ideas about science and medicine are built on the culture of ancient Greece.

1 **SUMMARIZING** Take notes using the Cornell Note Taking organizer below on the ideas of the ancient Greek philosophers. Summarize the sections and the images from your textbook to take notes.

Philosophers	Notes
Sophists	
Socrates	
Plato	
Aristotle	

2 **HISTORY** The Greek word *philosophy* means "love of wisdom." How does that help you understand ancient Greek culture?

_____

_____

_____

_____

_____

My Notes

_____

_____

_____

_____

_____

_____

3 ANALYZING Which Greek philosopher's work laid the groundwork for the study of science? Provide some examples of his studies.

_____

_____

_____

4 COMPARING AND CONTRASTING How were the historians Herodotus and Thucydides alike in their thinking, and how were they different?

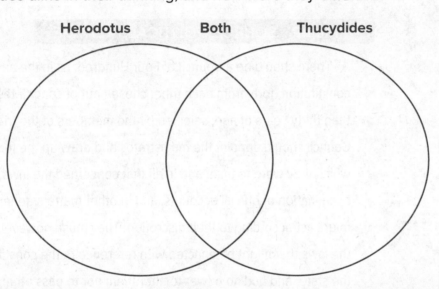

Herodotus   **Both**   **Thucydides**

5 DETERMINING CENTRAL IDEAS Important ancient Greek scientists are listed in the first column of the chart below. In the second column, write details explaining what each scientist is famous for.

Scientist	Major Contribution
Thales	
Pythagoras	
Hippocrates	

Athenian Constitution

DIRECTIONS: Study the following excerpt and answer the accompanying questions.

EXPLORE THE CONTEXT: Aristotle wrote many works on government. He was interested in how people interacted with their rulers. Each city in ancient Greece had its own system of government. In the passage below, Aristotle explains the political system of the ancient Greek city of Athens.

PRIMARY SOURCE: POLITICAL TREATISE

66 There should be a Council of Four Hundred, as in the ancient constitution, forty from each tribe, chosen out of candidates of more than thirty years of age, selected by the members of the tribes. This Council should appoint the magistrates and draw up the form of oath which they were to take; and in all that concerned the laws, in the examination of official accounts, and in other matters generally, they might act according to their discretion. They must, however, observe the laws that might be enacted with reference to the constitution of the state, and had no power to alter them nor to pass others. 99

— Aristotle, *The Athenian Constitution,* 350 B.C.E.

VOCABULARY

magistrate: judge

1 HISTORY What type of document is this? How does this information help you understand the document?

_____

_____

_____

_____

Copyright © McGraw-Hill Education; Thatcher, Oliver J. 1907. The Library of Original Sources - Editors Edition, Volume 2. New York, London, Chicago: University Research Extension.

2 EXPLAINING How were the members of the council chosen?

_____

_____

_____

_____

_____

_____

3 ANALYZING SOURCES What details from the source give information about the rules council members were required to follow?

_____

_____

_____

_____

_____

_____

_____

4 CIVICS What can you tell about the government of ancient Athens from the document?

_____

_____

_____

_____

_____

_____

Hippocrates

What makes a culture unique?

DIRECTIONS: Study the following excerpt and answer the accompanying questions.

EXPLORE THE CONTEXT: Hippocrates lived from around 460 to 370 B.C.E. He wrote many essays on medical issues. Some of his works include *On Injuries of the Head, On the Heart, On the Glands, On the Veins,* and *On the Diseases of Women.* He wrote so many essays on health and anatomy that he is sometimes called the "father of modern medicine." This excerpt is from his work called *Regimen in Acute Diseases.*

PRIMARY SOURCE: BOOK

❝ The course I recommend is to pay attention to the whole of the medical art. Indeed all acts that are good and correct should be in all cases well or correctly performed; if they ought to be done quickly, they should be done quickly, if neatly, neatly, if painlessly, they should be managed with a minimum of pain; and all such acts ought to be performed excellently, in a manner better than that of one's own fellows. ❞

— Hippocrates, *Regimen in Acute Diseases,* 400 B.C.E.

1 HISTORY What type of document is this? What does it help you understand?

_____

_____

_____

_____

2 ASKING QUESTIONS Does Hippocrates want something specific to happen by writing this document? What is his motive for writing?

_____

_____

_____

_____

_____

3 HISTORICAL CONTEXT When was the document written? How does that help you understand it?

_____

_____

_____

_____

_____

_____

4 HISTORICAL INFERENCE What inference can you make about Hippocrates from the details in the document? What evidence do you use to make your inference?

_____

_____

_____

_____

_____

ESSENTIAL QUESTION

What makes a culture unique?

As you gather evidence to answer the Essential Question, think about:

- how Phillip II of Macedonia changed the culture of ancient Greece.
- the role of Alexander the Great in ancient Greek culture.
- the culture of the Hellenistic Era.

My Notes

_____

_____

_____

_____

_____

_____

_____

_____

_____

_____

_____

Alexander's Empire

DIRECTIONS: Search for evidence in Chapter 6, Lesson 3 to help you answer the following questions.

1 **SEQUENCING** Use information from the text and the sequence of events organizer below to list events, beginning with the Macedonian conquest of ancient Greece to the period of the Hellenistic kings.

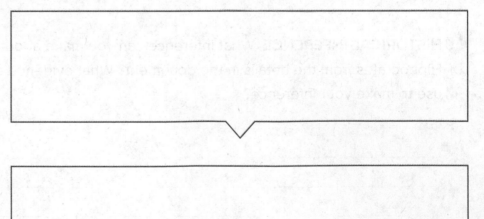

2 EXPLAINING CAUSE AND EFFECT Use the cause-and-effect organizer below to explain what caused Alexander the Great to come to power and the effect of his leadership.

3 `CIVICS` How did Alexander the Great and the later Hellenistic rulers spread ancient Greek culture?

_____

_____

_____

_____

_____

_____

What makes a culture unique?

Map of Alexander the Great's Territory

DIRECTIONS: Study the following image and answer the accompanying questions.

EXPLORE THE CONTEXT: Alexander the Great had a vision of uniting Macedonia, Greece, Egypt, and Asia Minor into one empire. The map in this image, created in 1862 C.E., marks the area that he ruled when he was at his greatest power.

SECONDARY SOURCE: MAP

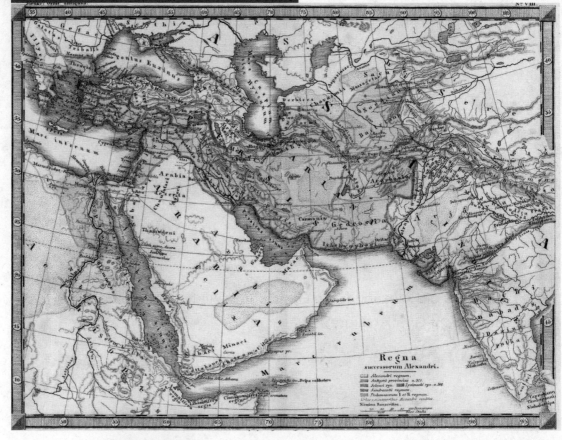

1 **GEOGRAPHY** What are the beneficial natural features that Alexander has access to in his vast territory?

_____

_____

_____

_____

_____

2 **GEOGRAPHY** How does the geography of Greece, the homeland of Hellenistic rule, present challenges for Alexander the Great's rule?

_____

_____

_____

_____

_____

3 **CIVICS** How does the vast territory with its challenging geographic features place limits on the government that Alexander the Great imagined?

_____

_____

_____

_____

_____

4 **CONNECT TO TODAY** Alexander the Great's empire stretched from the shores of the Mediterranean Sea and across southern Asia to the Indian subcontinent. Which modern-day countries within the boundaries of that ancient empire have been in the news lately? Name at least two countries and explain what has happened there.

_____

_____

_____

_____

_____

_____

On Alexander from the Works of Christina Queen of Sweden

DIRECTIONS: Study the following passage and answer the accompanying questions.

EXPLORE THE CONTEXT: Christina, Queen of Sweden, lived from 1626 to 1689 C.E. She became queen at age 6 when her warrior king father died. Christina was educated as a prince and cared deeply about reading and the arts. She loved exciting stories and admired Alexander the Great for his adventure and bravery.

SECONDARY SOURCE: BOOK EXCERPT

66 But this great, this invincible Alexander, who so well discharged the duties of his rank, however engrossed by ambition, however employed in great and important affairs, read almost as much as if he had been retired. Greece at that time, learned as it was, could not furnish him with books enough. Homer and his sword lay always by his side. He loved letters little less than glory. He favored every fine genius; he was liberal to profusion in encouraging arts and sciences, as appeared in many shining instances. . . . Philosophers, orators, poets, sculptors, and every able man in his age partook of his liberality and shared in his fortune. 99

—from *The Works of Christina Queen of Sweden*, 1753 C.E.

VOCABULARY

Homer: a Greek poet and his written works
profusion: large amount
orators: public speakers
partook: took part in
liberality: open-mindedness

1 **DETERMINING CONTEXT** Who wrote the passage? What was her occupation and background? How does this information help you understand the document?

_____

_____

_____

_____

2 **ANALYZING POINTS OF VIEW** How does the author describe Alexander the Great? What does she call out as his best qualities?

_____

_____

_____

_____

3 **ANALYZING SOURCES** When was the passage written? Where was it written? How does this information help you understand the credibility of the information in this document?

_____

_____

_____

_____

4 **DRAWING CONCLUSIONS** What was the author's purpose in writing about Alexander the Great's passion for cultural activities?

_____

_____

_____

_____

ESSENTIAL QUESTION

What makes a culture unique?

As you gather evidence to answer the Essential Question, think about:

- how poets and playwrights illustrate the culture of a society.
- the connection between happiness and reason.
- how mathematics and science reveal information about a culture.

My Notes

_____

_____

_____

_____

_____

_____

_____

_____

_____

Hellenistic Culture

DIRECTIONS: Search for evidence in Chapter 6, Lesson 4 to help you answer the following questions.

1 EXPLAINING CAUSE AND EFFECT For each effect listed in the graphic organizer below, write the cause of that effect.

Cause	Effect
	Alexandria became the Greek capital of Egypt.
	Hellenistic kings built public building projects.
	Hellenistic rulers supported talented writers.

2 **COMPARING AND CONTRASTING** Use the diagram below to compare and contrast Epicureanism and Stoicism. How are they alike, and how are they different?

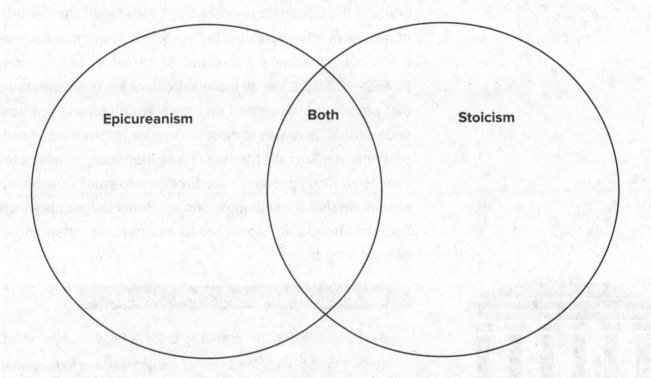

Epicureanism   Both   Stoicism

3 **SUMMARIZING** The Greek scientists and mathematicians made important discoveries in ancient Greece. Summarize what you learned about each figure on the lines that follow.

_____

_____

_____

_____

_____

_____

Stoicism

ESSENTIAL QUESTION
What makes a culture unique?

DIRECTIONS: Study the following excerpt, and answer the accompanying questions.

EXPLORE THE CONTEXT: The philosophy of Stoicism was developed by Zeno, who lived from 334 to 262 B.C.E. His ideas became the dominant philosophy of the Hellenistic period. None of his works have survived, but we know about him from the works of his followers. Zeno studied the works of Socrates (c. 469–399 B.C.E.) as all Hellenistic thinkers did. Zeno taught that people should control their own emotions and passions to find wisdom. Socrates is most known for his method of tackling a problem. His Socratic Method is a systematic process of teaching in which difficult problems are broken into small questions. In answering these small questions, students taught under the Socratic Method are slowly led to a better understanding of a subject or truth.

SECONDARY SOURCE: BOOK EXCERPT

66 The study of Stoicism cannot be properly begun without some attempt to trace its germs in earlier speculation, and to note what was the state of Greek society in which it first took root before it was transferred to other and perhaps to kindlier soils. Like all the famous systems which divided the earnest thinkers of the old Greek world, its real starting-point is to be found in the life and thought of Socrates, whose original and striking figure fills so marked a place in the pictures of the social life at Athens towards the close of the fifth century before our era. Not that Greek philosophy began with him. There had been no lack before of serious efforts to solve some of the many problems which had forced themselves upon men's thoughts when they looked out upon the universe around them, or tried to think about their own relations to the world unseen, and to the infinities that lay before and after. 99

— Rev. W.W. Capes, *Stoicism*, 1880 C.E.

VOCABULARY

germ: beginning
speculation: thought, theories
striking: impressive
infinities: endless unknowns

1 DETERMINING CONTEXT What type of document is this? How does knowing this help you understand the passage?

_____

_____

_____

_____

2 CITING TEXT EVIDENCE What point is the author making in his comparison of Stoicism to the ideas of Socrates? What evidence from the passage suggests that the author considers this point controversial?

_____

_____

_____

_____

_____

3 `HISTORY` Why was the passage written? How does the purpose for writing help you understand it?

_____

_____

_____

_____

4 DISTINGUISHING FACT FROM OPINION The author includes some of his own opinions in the passage. In his argument about the roots of Stoicism, the author mixes his opinions with established facts. Identify the opinions and the facts in the author's argument.

_____

_____

_____

_____

_____

_____

Winged Victory of Samothrace

DIRECTIONS: Study the following image and answer the accompanying questions.

EXPLORE THE CONTEXT: The statue pictured here is called the Winged Victory of Samothrace. It is a statue of the Goddess Nike from the Hellenistic period, probably created around 200 B.C.E. to honor a naval battle at the Greek island of Samothrace. Nike is the ancient Greek Goddess of victory. The statue now stands in a famous museum in Paris, France, called the Louvre. Although historians have preserved Roman copies of Hellenistic statues, this Winged Victory of Samothrace is one of the few original sculptures from that period.

PRIMARY SOURCE: STATUE

1 HISTORY Describe the statue pictured in this image. What does its appearance help you understand about the work of art and the culture it came from?

_____

_____

_____

_____

_____

2 INFERRING We know that the statue honors the Goddess of victory on the occasion of a battle triumph. What does this fact help you understand about the values of the ancient Greeks?

_____

_____

_____

3 HISTORY What was happening in the region during the 200s B.C.E. that influenced the creation of this statue?

_____

_____

_____

_____

4 CIVICS The Winged Victory of Samothrace is held in a famous museum and considered one of the world's treasures. What does this fact say about western culture today?

_____

_____

_____

_____

1 Think About It

Review the supporting questions you developed at the opening of the chapter. Review the evidence you found in Chapter 6. Were you able to answer each of your Supporting Questions?

If you didn't find enough evidence to answer your Supporting Questions, what do you think you need to consider?

_____

_____

_____

_____

_____

2 Organize Your Evidence

Use a web like the one below to organize the evidence you will use to support your Position Statement.

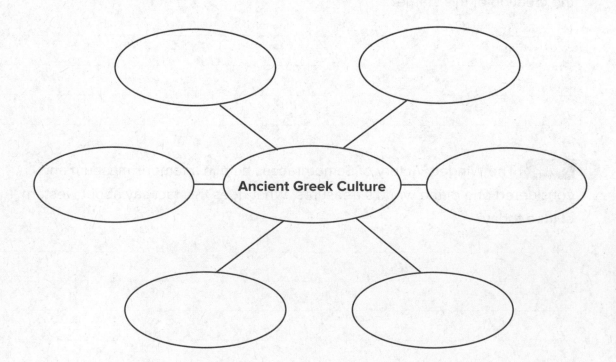

Ancient Greek Culture

❸ Talk About It

Discuss the evidence you have gathered with a small group or partner. Check your group's understanding of the qualities that make a culture unique, and answer any questions members may have. Consider any additional advice or input they may have.

❹ Connect to the Essential Question

On a separate piece of paper, write a scene for a play in the style of a Greek tragedy or comedy. Include information about the culture of ancient Greece and details that reveal how it made ancient Greek culture unique. Your scene should answer the ESSENTIAL QUESTION: *What makes a culture unique?*

CITIZENSHIP
TAKING ACTION

MAKE CONNECTIONS In ancient Greece, culture thrived, and poets and playwrights became important, famous people. Today, ancient Greek poetry and drama remain part of Western culture. We are able to understand the day-to-day lives of the ancient Greeks, the issues they cared deeply about, and their values through their literature. Yet the window into a culture through literature is not unique to ancient Greece. That window exists for most cultures that have a well-developed literary tradition. This includes the United States today. Although you may not read poetry every day, there are countless modern American poets who capture the feeling, frustrations, and triumphs of modern culture through verse and drama.

DIRECTIONS: Use what you have learned about what makes a culture unique to participate in a modern poetry reading. Research modern American poets and select a poem or short work of literature that captures an idea about the culture you experience today. Then take turns among your classmates to read your selection aloud. Discuss as a class how the details of the poem you chose reveal information about the culture today.

_____

_____

_____

_____

_____

_____

_____

Ancient India

ESSENTIAL QUESTION

What makes a culture unique?

Think about how this question might relate to ancient India.

TALK ABOUT IT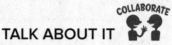

Discuss with a partner what type of information you would need to know to answer this question. For example, one question might be: What factors contributed to the development of ancient Indian culture that set it apart from other cultures?

DIRECTIONS: Now write three additional questions that would help you explain what made ancient Indian culture unique.

MY RESEARCH QUESTIONS

Supporting Question 1:

_____

_____

Supporting Question 2:

_____

_____

Supporting Question 3:

_____

_____

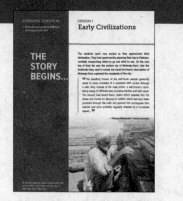

Early Civilizations

DIRECTIONS: Search for evidence in Chapter 7, Lesson 1 to help you answer the following questions.

1 EXPLAINING CAUSE AND EFFECT How did geography and climate influence ancient cultures in India?

_____
_____
_____
_____
_____
_____
_____

ESSENTIAL QUESTION

What makes a culture unique?

As you gather evidence to answer the Essential Question, think about:

- the landforms and climate of India's subcontinent.
- development of ancient cultures along the Indus and the later impact of the Aryans.

My Notes

_____
_____
_____
_____
_____
_____
_____
_____

2 HISTORY Describe the elements responsible for progress in the Indus civilization. Use the text's discussion of these elements and the chart below to help you organize the facts.

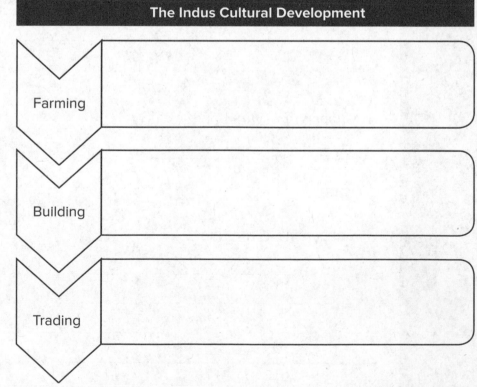

The Indus Cultural Development

Farming

Building

Trading

3 **RELATING EVENTS** How did the Aryans influence the culture of India? Use the organizing web to show the various ways Aryans influenced India.

4 CIVICS How did the varnas affect ancient Indians and their civic choices?

_____

_____

_____

_____

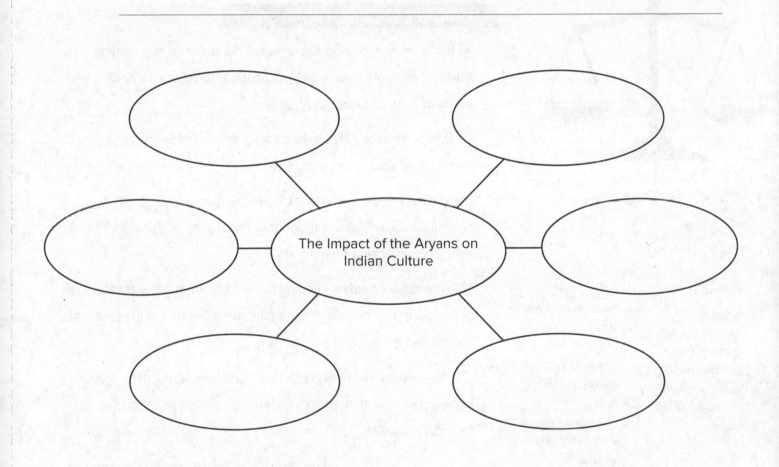

The Impact of the Aryans on Indian Culture

The Laws of Manu

ESSENTIAL QUESTION

What makes a culture unique?

DIRECTIONS: Study the excerpt below and answer the accompanying questions.

EXPLORE THE CONTEXT: The Laws of Manu are believed to have been written around 200 C.E. They contain one of Asia's first written codes of law, both moral and religious. The laws were specific and detailed about how class or varna relationships were to be conducted in India.

PRIMARY SOURCE: LEGAL CODE

❝ But in order to protect this universe He, the most resplendent one, assigned separate (duties and) occupations to those who sprang from his mouth, arms, thighs, and feet.

91. One occupation only the lord prescribed to the Sudra, to serve meekly even these (other) three castes. . . .

127. (Sudras) who are desirous to gain merit, and know (their) duty, commit no sin, but gain praise, if they imitate the practice of virtuous men without reciting sacred texts.

128. The more a (Sudra), keeping himself free from envy, imitates the behaviour of the virtuous, the more he gains, without being censured, (exaltation in) this world and the next.

129. No collection of wealth must be made by a Sudra, even though he be able (to do it); for a Sudra who has acquired wealth, gives pain to Brahmanas. ❞

—from *The Laws of Manu* (Sacred Books of the East, Volume 25)

VOCABULARY

resplendent: magnificent, with glowing light
prescribed: assigned
caste: assigned position or social status

merit: spiritual credit
virtuous: principled, moral
censured: criticized
exaltation: honor, praise
Brahmanas: sacred writings about the Vedas

1 DETERMINING POINT OF VIEW Discuss this excerpt with a partner. Whose point of view is being proclaimed? Does this suggest that there are other points of view to be considered? Use evidence from the text to support your answers.

COLLABORATE

_____

_____

_____

2 `ECONOMICS` How did the Laws of Manu impact the economy of the Sudra? Would the greater economy of India also have been impacted? Support your answer with details using the text and the excerpt.

_____

_____

_____

_____

3 ANALYZING TEXT How does the first sentence of instruction (91) contribute to the development of these rules for the Sudra? Explain, citing references in the text.

_____

_____

_____

_____

4 DETERMINING MEANING Based on the excerpt, what is the only hope of the Sudra who follows the Laws of Manu? Use details to support your answer.

_____

_____

_____

Life in Harappa and Mohenjo-Daro

DIRECTIONS: Study the excerpt below and answer the accompanying questions.

EXPLORE THE CONTEXT: This excerpt is from a study on the ancient cities of Harappa and Mohenjo-Daro. It takes a look at the archaeological evidence and provides insights into what life might have been like when the cities thrived.

SECONDARY SOURCE: BOOK EXCERPT

66 The ruins of Harappa and Mohenjo-Daro reveal that they were the products of the first city planning in history. Wide, straight streets divide residential areas into square city blocks. Archaeologists have excavated houses, granaries, public halls, and shops. Both cities had extensive sewer systems. Walled fortresses with towers provided protection. To create such well-planned cities, the people needed a knowledge of surveying and geometry. Furthermore, only a strong central government in each city could have supervised the planning and construction. Scholars are not sure who ruled the Indus Valley cities, but they think that a priest-king probably headed the government of each city. The rulers must have had considerable power because the governments exercised strict control. For example, they controlled construction of new buildings and established standards of weight and measures. Because of the tight control, writing, building styles, street plans, and even the size of bricks remained unchanged for nearly 1,000 years. . . . Evidence from the diggings shows that the Indus Valley civilization began to decline many years before it finally ended about 1500 B.C. Builders abandoned the uniform standards of earlier times, and quality of work declined. The arts showed less creativity, and trade with Mesopotamia dwindled. 99

—from *World History: Patterns of Civilization* by Burton Beers, 1990 C.E.

VOCABULARY

archaeologists: people who study earlier cultures by examining their artifacts and writings

excavated: dug holes in the earth to find remains of cultures

granaries: storage buildings for harvested grain

extensive: wide and broad in size

surveying: figuring the exact size and form of something using mathematics, geometry, and trigonometry

decline: weaken

uniform: all the same; consistent

dwindled: decreased

1 **EVALUATING ARGUMENTS** What evidence does the author use to suggest the cities had strong, powerful governments?

_____

_____

_____

2 **COMPARING AND CONTRASTING TEXTS** How is this excerpt similar to the text description of Mahenjo-Daro and Harappa? How are the two sources different?

_____

_____

_____

_____

_____

_____

3 GEOGRAPHY **AND** HISTORY Considering the geography and history of these great cities, what might have led to their ruin? List evidence from your text and the excerpt that supports your ideas.

_____

_____

_____

_____

_____

_____

4 **MAKING CONNECTIONS** The excerpt notes that the quality of work declined in these ancient cities once uniform standards were abandoned. Give examples of how uniform standards help ensure quality in the United States today.

_____

_____

ESSENTIAL QUESTION

What makes a culture unique?

As you gather evidence to answer the Essential Question, think about:

- how religions and philosophies are established.
- how beliefs and philosophies influence the way people live.

My Notes

Religions of Ancient India

DIRECTIONS: Search for evidence in Chapter 7, Lesson 2 to help you answer the following questions.

1 **EXPLAINING CAUSE AND EFFECT** How did the Hindu belief in reincarnation contribute to people's acceptance of the *jati* system?

_____

_____

_____

_____

_____

_____

2 **COMPARING AND CONTRASTING** How does Hinduism compare or contrast with Buddhism in the belief about how to live life successfully? Use the chart below to organize your answer.

BELIEFS ABOUT HOW TO LIVE SUCCESSFULLY	
Hinduism	
Buddhism	

3 ECONOMICS Complete the following chart to analyze the relationship between religion and economics in ancient India. Use details from the text to complete the chart.

Religions	What were the core beliefs of each religion, and how did they influence India's economy?
Hinduism	
Buddhism	
Jainism	

4 **ANALYZING IDEAS** What is a similar belief in both Hinduism and Jainism that shaped the way Hindus and Jains live? Cite details from the text to support your ideas.

_____

_____

_____

Jain Ethics

Copyright © McGraw-Hill Education; Shah, Pravin K. 1993. Twelve Vows of Layperson. Jain Study Center of North Carolina.

ESSENTIAL QUESTION

What makes a culture unique?

DIRECTIONS: Study the excerpt below and answer the accompanying questions.

EXPLORE THE CONTEXT: There were five challenging vows the monks had to follow in order to be spiritual leaders of the Jain teachings. The monks had to be free from relationships with their families and with everything of the world. For those followers of the faith who remained in their families, there were twelve specific, but easier, vows to follow.

SECONDARY SOURCE: BOOK EXCERPT

Non-violence Anuvrat (small vow)

66 In this vow, a person must not intentionally hurt any living being (plants, animals, humans etc.) or their feeling either by thought, word or deed, himself, or through others, or by approving such an act committed by somebody else. Intention in this case applies selfish motive, sheer pleasure and even avoidable negligence. He may use force, if necessary, in the defense of his country, society, family, life, property, religious institute.

His agricultural, industrial, occupational living activities do also involve injury to life, but it should be as minimum as possible, through carefulness and due precaution. 99

— Ahimsa Anuvrata, c. 500s B.C.E. quoted in *Twelve Vows of Layperson*, compiled by Pavin K. Shah, 1993 C.E.

VOCABULARY

ethics: principles of morality

layperson: a follower as opposed to leader

intentionally: on purpose

motive: the reason behind an action

negligence: ignoring a problem; carelessness

institute: a place where work is carried on

occupational: relating to a person's employment

1 **ANALYZING TEXT** What does the word *intentionally* mean? What does the use of this word mean for those taking this vow? Explain your answer using details from the excerpt.

_____

_____

_____

_____

2 **EXPLAINING POINTS OF VIEW** What does the Jain vow have in common with the Buddhist Eightfold Path and the Hindu belief in reincarnation and karma? Support your answer with evidence from Lesson 2.

_____

_____

_____

_____

_____

_____

_____

3 Which part of the vow makes it possible for Jains to serve in the military?

_____

_____

4 **MAKING CONNECTIONS** How would a commitment to be kinder to one another change the environment of your school?

_____

_____

_____

ESSENTIAL QUESTION

What makes a culture unique?

Nidāna: The Words of Disburdenment

DIRECTIONS: Study the excerpt below and answer the accompanying questions.

EXPLORE THE CONTEXT: *The Twelve Nidānas* are Buddhist writings that show cause-and-effect relationships between each of their twelve doctrines. In Sanskrit, the term *nidāna* means "motivation" or "link between things." The writings of Theravada Buddhism are written in Pâli, a language that developed in northern India between the fifth and second centuries B.C.E.

SECONDARY SOURCE: BOOK EXCERPT

Reverence to the Blessed One, the Holy One, the Fully Enlightened One: *Nidana: The Words of Disburdenment*

❝Now, venerable Sirs, it is by your silence, that I shall know whether you are pure. As to each one question put there must be an answer, so, in such a meeting as this, each question is put as many as three times. Then if any Bhikkhu, when it has been three times put, knowingly omit to declare a fault incurred, he is guilty of uttering a conscious lie. Venerable Sirs, the uttering of a deliberate lie has been declared by the Blessed One to be a condition hurtful (to spiritual progress). Therefore a fault, if there be one, should be declared by that Bhikkhu who remembers it, and desires to be cleansed therefrom. For a fault, when declared, shall be light to him.

Venerable Sirs, the Introduction is now recited.

Thus do I question you, venerable Sirs, 'Are you pure in this matter?'

A second time do I question you, 'Are you pure in this matter?'

A third time do I question you, 'Are you pure in this matter?'

The venerable ones are pure herein. Therefore do they keep silence. Thus I understand.❞

— Siddhartha Gautama, c. 500 B.C.E., as recorded in *The Pâtimokkha, Vol. XIII of The Sacred Books of the East,* translated from Pâli by T.W. Rhys Davids and Hermann Oldenberg

VOCABULARY

reverence: deep respect or awe

enlightened: having achieved knowledge through spiritual practice

disburdenment: the removal of a burden or a problem

venerable: worthy of respect because of age or spiritual status

bhikkhu: a male Buddhist monk, or spiritual teacher

incurred: brought upon oneself

uttering: speaking

1 ANALYZING IDEAS Analyze how the writer introduced the topic. Describe the central idea. Where did you locate it? How did the writer make the central idea clear through examples or supporting details?

_____

_____

_____

_____

_____

_____

_____

_____

_____

_____

_____

_____

_____

_____

_____

_____

_____

_____

_____

_____

_____

ESSENTIAL QUESTION

What makes a culture unique?

2 **COMPARING AND CONTRASTING TEXTS** Examine the description of Buddhist beliefs in Lesson 2. Does this excerpt match what you read? Explain whether the ideas in the two sources are in agreement or not, and support with text evidence.

_____

_____

_____

_____

_____

_____

_____

_____

_____

_____

3 CIVICS   How might this Buddhist principle apply to government and citizenship? Explain your ideas.

_____

_____

_____

_____

_____

_____

_____

_____

_____

_____

_____

DETERMINING MEANING What purpose do you believe was served by the repetition of the questions at the end? Explain your ideas.

_____

_____

_____

_____

_____

_____

_____

_____

_____

_____

_____

The Mauryan Empire

DIRECTIONS: Search for evidence in Chapter 7, Lesson 3 to help you answer the following questions.

ESSENTIAL QUESTION

What makes a culture unique?

As you gather evidence to answer the Essential Question, think about:

- the development of the Mauryan and Gupta dynasties in ancient India.

- the contributions of the Mauryan and Gupta Empires to the Indian culture.

1 **IDENTIFYING CAUSE AND EFFECT** What events set Chandragupta Maurya in place as ruler of the Mauryan dynasty?

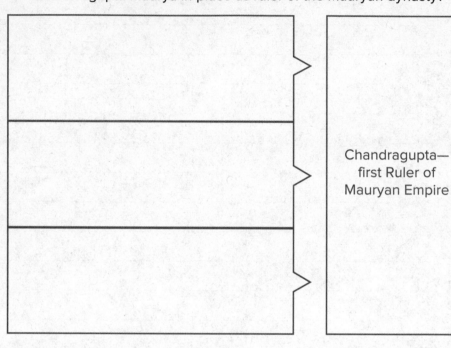

Chandragupta— first Ruler of Mauryan Empire

2 **ANALYZING IDEAS** Analyze the methods the Mauryan king Ashoka used to govern his kingdom and how his ideas affected Indian culture. Use the chart below to organize your information, citing references from Lesson 3.

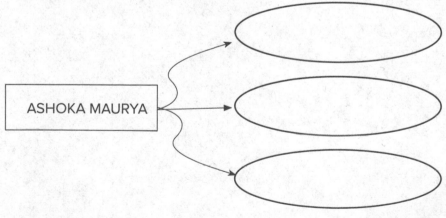

ASHOKA MAURYA

My Notes

_____

_____

_____

_____

_____

_____

_____

_____

_____

3 HISTORY How did the Mauryan rulers who followed Ashoka govern India? What were the consequences of their rule for the Mauryan Empire? Explain.

_____

_____

_____

_____

4 **DETERMINING CENTRAL IDEAS** What influence did the Mauryan and Gupta Empires have on Indian culture? Collect details from your text. Use the chart below to organize your information, and then write a central idea statement.

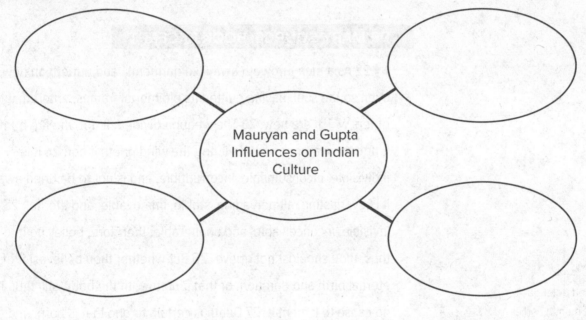

Mauryan and Gupta Influences on Indian Culture

_____

_____

The Bhagavad Gita

ESSENTIAL QUESTION

What makes a culture unique?

DIRECTIONS: Study the excerpt below and answer the accompanying questions.

EXPLORE THE CONTEXT: *The Bhagavad Gita* is a 700-verse Hindu scripture composed in Sanskrit, often referred to as "the Divine Song." It is part of an epic poem that is considered the longest in the world. Sections are broken out into numbered lines, often called verses. Historians believe the *Bhagavad Gita* was recorded in writing between 400 B.C.E. and 200 C.E.

PRIMARY SOURCE: BOOK EXCERPT

❝ 22 As a man throweth away old garments, and putteth on new, even so the soul, having quitted its old mortal frames, entereth into others which are new. 23 The weapon divideth it not, the fire burneth it not, the water corrupteth it not, the wind drieth it not; 24 It is indivisible, inconsumable, incorruptible, and is not to be dried away: it is everlasting, all-pervading, stable, immovable, and eternal; 25 it is invisible, inconceivable, and unalterable; therefore, believing it to be thus, thou shouldst not grieve. 26 But whether thou believest it of eternal birth and duration, or that it dieth with the body, still thou hast no cause to lament it. 27 Death is certain to one that is born, and to one that dieth birth is certain. Wherefore it doth not behove thee to grieve about that which is inevitable. 28 The former state of beings is unknown; the middle state is evident, and their future state is not to be discovered. Why then shouldst thou trouble thyself about such things as these? 29 Some regard the soul as a wonder, whilst some speak and others hear of it with astonishment; but no one knoweth it, although he may have heard it described. ❞

— from *The Bhagavad Gita*

VOCABULARY

quitted: released or let go

mortal frames: human bodies

indivisible: incapable of being divided or separated

inconsumable: cannot be used up

incorruptible: unable to be spoiled or corrupted

all-pervading: spread throughout

inconceivable: unable to be understood

unalterable: unchanging

lament: grieve or regret

behove: fit or suit a person

inevitable: sure to happen

1 **DETERMINING MEANING** How does the writer support his idea that when the human frame (the body) is finished, the soul (the spiritual or emotional part) is not?

_____

_____

_____

2 **ANALYZING POINT OF VIEW** What lines in the excerpt explain the writer's beliefs about rebirth, or reincarnation?

_____

_____

_____

_____

_____

3 **ANALYZING TEXT** Why does the writer believe it is foolish to worry about death?

_____

_____

_____

_____

4 HISTORY What historic developments contributed to the writing of the *Bhagavad Gita*, and how might this excerpt have fit into the story? Cite evidence from Lesson 3 to support your answer.

_____

_____

_____

_____

_____

_____

The Iron Pillar near Delhi, India

DIRECTIONS: Examine the image below and answer the accompanying questions.

EXPLORE THE CONTEXT: The large iron pillar from the Gupta period is remarkable not only because of its size (about 23 feet, or 7 meters, tall), but because its metal is resistant to rust. The ancient writing on it remains well-preserved, and readable. The pillar was created around 400 C.E.

PRIMARY SOURCE: PHOTOGRAPH

1 **INTEGRATING VISUAL INFORMATION** Based on information from Lesson 3 and the photograph of the Iron Pillar, why do you think this pillar may have been built?

_____

_____

_____

2 **HISTORY** How does the pillar compare to other iron works from its era in size, structure, and resistance to rust? Use information in Lesson 3 to help you explain why this pillar is considered noteworthy.

_____

_____

_____

_____

_____

_____

3 **DRAWING CONCLUSIONS** What does the pillar suggest about the culture of the Gupta era? Explain.

_____

_____

_____

_____

4 **MAKING CONNECTIONS** If you saw a similar monument in Washington, D.C., what would you think about the builder's purpose? What might be inscribed on it?

_____

_____

_____

1 Think About It

Review the Supporting Questions that you developed at the beginning of the chapter. Review the evidence that you gathered in Chapter 7. Were you able to answer each Supporting Question?

If there was not enough evidence to answer your Supporting Questions, what additional evidence do you think you need?

_____

_____

_____

2 Organize Your Evidence

Use the chart to organize the evidence you will use to support your Position Statement.

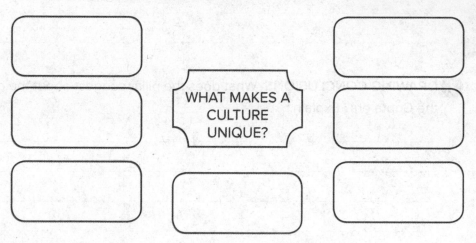

WHAT MAKES A CULTURE UNIQUE?

❸ Talk About It

Work with a partner or small group to discuss your position statement and the evidence you have gathered. Before you write your final conclusion, gather ideas from your classmates. Group members should take turns sharing their ideas, asking questions, and offering insights. Use your lesson readings to guide you as you support your ideas.

❹ Write About It

Write your position statement for the ESSENTIAL QUESTION, using your gathered information: *What makes a culture unique?*

_____

_____

_____

_____

_____

_____

❺ Connect to the Essential Question

On a separate piece of paper, create a visual essay. Use the organizer from question 2 to prepare your case explaining how Indian culture is unique. Either draw pictures to represent the various influences that helped shape ancient Indian culture or find photographs to copy and insert into your essay.

CITIZENSHIP
TAKING ACTION

MAKE CONNECTIONS Think about how the culture of your community impacts how you and your family live. What are the most important influences in your area that shape your personal culture?

DIRECTIONS: What is a belief you hold that is also important in your community's culture? How can you become involved in promoting this belief? Promote what you feel should be changed to make life better or to spread your belief. Promote your belief by choosing one of these ideas: organize a rally, write and perform a song about it, or create a promotional advertisement.

_____
_____
_____
_____
_____
_____
_____
_____
_____
_____
_____
_____

CHAPTER 8

Early China

ESSENTIAL QUESTION

What makes a culture unique?

Think about how this question might relate to the culture of ancient China.

TALK ABOUT IT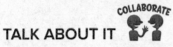

Discuss with a partner what type of information you would need to know to answer this question. For example, one question might be: What factors made the culture of early China different from the culture of its neighbors?

DIRECTIONS: Now write three additional questions that would help you explain the distinctive characteristics of early Chinese culture.

MY RESEARCH QUESTIONS

Supporting Question 1:

_____

_____

Supporting Question 2:

_____

_____

Supporting Question 3:

_____

_____

The Birth Of Chinese Civilization

DIRECTIONS: Search for evidence in Chapter 8, Lesson 1 to help you answer the following questions.

ESSENTIAL QUESTION

What makes a culture unique?

As you gather evidence to answer the Essential Question, think about:

- the rivers, mountains, and deserts that separated ancient China from other civilizations.
- the power of the dynasty kings over those they ruled.

1 **EXPLAINING CAUSE AND EFFECT** How did the geography of China help determine its development?

_____

_____

_____

_____

_____

2 **CITING TEXT EVIDENCE** Record supporting details to explain the idea that religion and government were related during the Shang dynasty.

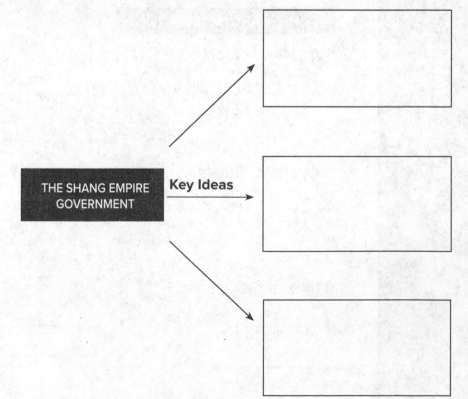

THE SHANG EMPIRE GOVERNMENT　**Key Ideas**

My Notes

_____

_____

_____

_____

_____

_____

_____

_____

3 **ANALYZING EVENTS** What were the significant events that allowed the Zhou dynasty to rule China for more than 800 years? Use the organizer to record important ideas that shaped the culture under the Zhou reign.

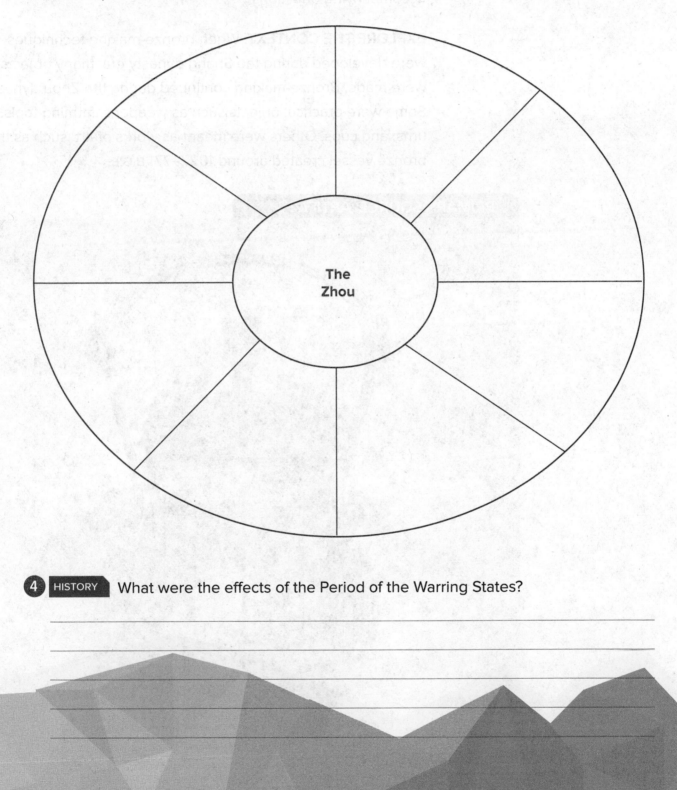

The
Zhou

4 **HISTORY** What were the effects of the Period of the Warring States?

_____

_____

_____

_____

_____

Bronze From Early Zhou Dynasty

ESSENTIAL QUESTION

What makes a culture unique?

DIRECTIONS: Examine the artifact below and answer the accompanying questions.

EXPLORE THE CONTEXT: When bronze-making techniques were developed during the Shang dynasty era, many objects were made. Bronze-making continued during the Zhou dynasty. Some were practical objects such as weapons, farming tools, urns, and cups. Others were meant as works of art, such as this bronze vessel created around 1027–771 B.C.E.

PRIMARY SOURCE: ARTIFACT

1 **INTEGRATING VISUAL INFORMATION** Reread the text about bronze making and closely examine the object. Note the body of the vessel and the decorated elements, including the lid. What do you think this object may have been used for?

_____

_____

_____

_____

2 ECONOMY What do you think such a piece of bronze tells about the development of the Zhou culture economically?

_____

_____

_____

_____

3 **INTEGRATING VISUAL INFORMATION** Who would have been the most likely users of this kind of a bronze vessel during the Zhou dynasty?

_____

_____

_____

_____

4 HISTORY This bronze container was developed sometime during the lengthy 800-year Zhou reign. From the text, is there a period during which you think it is more or less likely that it would have been made?

_____

_____

_____

_____

Teachings of Confucius

Copyright © McGraw-Hill Education; Confucius. Translated 1900 by William Jennings, James Legge, John Francis Davis, and Epiphanius Wilson. Chinese Literature Comprising The Analects of Confucius, The Shi-King, The Sayings of Mencius, The Sorrows of Han, and The Travels of Fâ-Hien. London & New York: The Colonial Press.

ESSENTIAL QUESTION
What makes a culture unique?

DIRECTIONS: Read the following excerpt and answer the accompanying questions.

EXPLORE THE CONTEXT: This excerpt from an anonymous collection of quotations (compiled c. 475 B.C.E.—221 B.C.E.) provides insight into the mind of Confucius and his teachings.

PRIMARY SOURCE: BOOK EXCERPT

"'One should not be greatly concerned at not being in office; but rather about the requirements in one's self for such a standing. Neither should one be so much concerned at being unknown; but rather with seeking to become worthy of being known.'

Addressing his disciple Tsang Sin, the Master said, 'Tsang Sin, the principles which I inculcate have one main idea upon which they all hang.' 'Aye, surely,' he replied.

When the Master was gone out the other disciples asked what was the purport of this remark. Tsang's answer was, 'The principles of our Master's teaching are these—whole-heartedness and kindly forbearance; these and nothing more.' "

—from *Chinese Literature Comprising The Analects of Confucius, The Sayings of Mencius, The Shi-King, The Travels of Fâ-Hien, and The Sorrows of Han*

VOCABULARY

standing: rank or position; how others regard you
disciple: follower, student, learner
inculcate: consistently teach
aye: a word that shows agreement
purport: meaning or sense
whole-heartedness: with full support
forbearance: complete self-control

1 ANALYZING What does Confucius believe should be the highest concern of those who hold office, or wish they could?

_____

_____

_____

_____

2 INFERRING If Confucius had convinced the aristocrats, kings, and royal officials to live according to his philosophy, how would that have affected the dynasties?

_____

_____

_____

_____

3 DETERMINING MEANING Use the text to help you explain what Confucius means by "seeking to become worthy of being known."

_____

_____

_____

_____

4 MAKING CONNECTIONS If you heard a teacher today say something similar, what would you think about his or her purpose? Explain your answer.

_____

_____

_____

_____

5 IDENTIFYING Underline the phrases that refer to the central idea of Confucius's teaching.

_____

_____

Society and Culture in Ancient China

DIRECTIONS: Search for evidence in Chapter 8, Lesson 2 to help you answer the following questions.

ESSENTIAL QUESTION

What makes a culture unique?

As you gather evidence to answer the Essential Question, think about:

- the impact that the philosophies of Confucius, Laozi, and Hanfeizi had on China.

- the effect class structure had on early China and the way people lived.

1 EXPLAINING CAUSE AND EFFECT How did the different philosophies help shape the culture of early China?

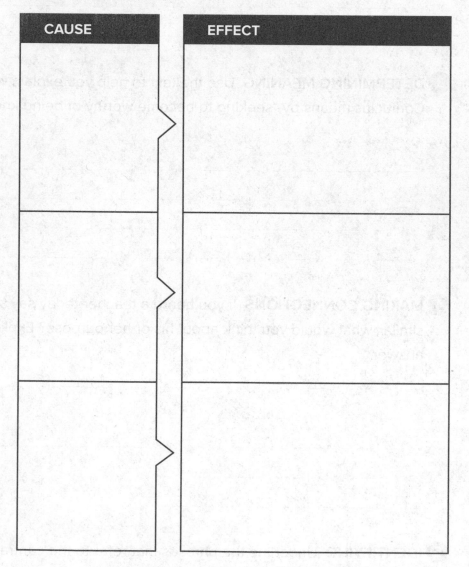

CAUSE	EFFECT

My Notes

_____

_____

_____

_____

_____

_____

_____

_____

2 **CITING TEXT EVIDENCE** Analyze the four Chinese social classes using evidence from the text.

Aristocrats	Farmers	Artisans	Merchants

3 **COMPARING AND CONTRASTING** How were the roles of men and women similar and different in early China?

The Roles of Men and Women in Early China	
Similarities:	Differences:

4 ECONOMICS How did the practice of children inheriting land from their parents affect the income of the aristocratic families? What was the economic consequence to the land-owning families after several generations?

_____

_____

_____

The Tao and Its Characteristics

ESSENTIAL QUESTION
What makes a culture unique?

DIRECTIONS: Study the following excerpt and answer the accompanying questions.

EXPLORE THE CONTEXT: Laozi is believed to be the founder of the philosophy known as Daoism and is accepted as the author of the Dao, writings about these beliefs. This excerpt from his writings will reveal some core ideas that influenced the early Chinese culture.

PRIMARY SOURCE: BOOK EXCERPT

❝46. 1. When the Tao prevails in the world, they send back their swift horses to (draw) the dung-carts. When the Tao is disregarded in the world, the war-horses breed in the border lands.

2. There is no guilt greater than to sanction ambition; no calamity greater than to be discontented with one's lot; no fault greater than the wish to be getting. Therefore the sufficiency of contentment is an enduring and unchanging sufficiency.

49. 1. The sage has no invariable mind of his own; he makes the mind of the people his mind.

2. To those who are good (to me), I am good; and to those who are not good (to me), I am also good;—and thus (all) get to be good. To those who are sincere (with me), I am sincere; and to those who are not sincere (with me), I am also sincere;—and thus (all) get to be sincere.

3. The sage has in the world an appearance of indecision, and keeps his mind in a state of indifference to all. The people all keep their eyes and ears directed to him, and he deals with them all as his children. ❞

— Lao-Tse [Laozi], *The Tao Teh King, or The Tao and Its Characteristics, Part II,* c. 700s B.C.E.—200s B.C.E.

VOCABULARY

Tao: in Taoism, *Tao* refers to "the way," or right path of life (also spelled *Dao* and *Daoism*)
prevails: succeeds
dung-carts: carts used in farming to haul animal manure
sanction: approve
calamity: disaster
sufficiency: the state of having enough
enduring: lasting, constant
sage: wise person
invariable: unchanging

Copyright © McGraw-Hill Education; Lao Dze (Lao Tsu). 1891. Translated by Legge, James. Edited by Muller, F. Max. The Texts of Taoism - The Tao Teh King (Tao Te Ching). Oxford University Press.

1 CITING TEXT EVIDENCE According to the Tao, what are positive effects of living the "right path"? Write only the key ideas.

_____

_____

_____

2 COMPARING AND CONTRASTING How does this short excerpt from the Tao compare and contrast with the ideas of Laozi found in Chapter 8, Lesson 2?

_____

_____

_____

_____

_____

_____

3 ANALYZING POINTS OF VIEW Discuss with a partner the point of view of Laozi in verse 49:2. What message do you believe the sage is sending?

_____

_____

_____

_____

4 MAKING CONNECTIONS If you heard the philosophy of living peacefully with sincerity toward all people today, what would you think about the teacher's goal?

_____

_____

5 DRAWING CONCLUSIONS Why would the swift horses be used to pull dung-carts if people followed the teachings of Tao?

_____

_____

Copyright © McGraw-Hill Education; Ban, Zhao. 1900. Translated by Mrs. S. L. Baldwin. The Chinese Book of Etiquette For Women And Girls, Entitled, Instruction For Chinese Women And Girls. New York: Eaton & Mains.

ESSENTIAL QUESTION
What makes a culture unique?

Instruction on Conduct for Chinese Women and Girls

DIRECTIONS: Study the following excerpt and answer the accompanying questions.

EXPLORE THE CONTEXT: The author of this instruction manual for women and girls in early China was a daughter of a high official living during the Han dynasty. She was well known for her literary achievements at the time. Here she offers advice to young women regarding the roles of women in China at this time.

PRIMARY SOURCE: BOOK EXCERPT

Woman's Work.—Weaving Silk, etc.

❝All girls, everywhere, should learn woman's work. In weaving cloth, distinguish between the coarse and fine; When sitting at the loom, work carefully; when boiling the silk cocoons, collecting for them the mulberry and chia leaves, in all be very diligent. Protect the worms from wind and rain. If cold, warm them by the fire; keep them in a clean place. As the young ones grow, transfer them to baskets, but crowd them not; provide them leaves, not too many nor too few.

Making silk, be careful of the straight and cross threads, so you will make a perfect piece. When finished remove the gauze at once from the loom. Cotton cloth, fold and lay in boxes or baskets. Silk, cotton, and the two kinds of grass cloth, all learn perfectly to make, then you can sell to others, and yourself have clothing to wear. . . .

Do not imitate lazy women who from youth to womanhood have been stupid; not having exerted themselves in woman's work. They are prepared for neither cold nor warm weather. Their sewing is so miserable, people both laugh at and despise them. The idle girl, going forth to be married, injures the reputation of her husband's whole family. Her clothes are ragged and dirty. . . . She is a disgrace to her village. I thus exhort and warn the girls, let them hear and learn.❞

—from *The Chinese Book of Etiquette and Conduct for Women and Girls*, c. 49 C.E.—120 C.E.

VOCABULARY

distinguish: recognize the differences
diligent: untiring, hardworking
cross threads: the crosswise or horizontal threads in weaving
gauze: lightweight woven fabric, usually of cotton or silk
idle: lacking in effort; lazy
exhort: caution; encourage to do something

1 **COMPARING AND CONTRASTING** How does the description of filial piety in Chapter 8, Lesson 2 compare or contrast with the excerpt about the conduct of women and girls?

_____

_____

_____

2 **ANALYZING POINTS OF VIEW** According to the author, what character traits should girls and women conform to?

_____

_____

_____

3 **MAKING CONNECTIONS** If you read instructions for today's girls that had the same tone as these, what would be your reaction? What parts might you agree with, and how might you disagree?

_____

_____

_____

_____

4 **ECONOMICS** How would this set of instructions contribute to the economy of early China?

_____

_____

_____

_____

5 **DRAWING CONCLUSIONS** From examining the central idea in this excerpt, what can you conclude was the primary role of girls and women in early China?

_____

_____

_____

The Qin and Han Dynasties

DIRECTIONS: Search for evidence in Chapter 8, Lesson 3 to help you answer the following questions.

ESSENTIAL QUESTION

What makes a culture unique?

As you gather evidence to answer the Essential Question, think about:

- how the Qin emperor brought changes to the Chinese culture when he took control.

- the impact of the new government and time of peace during the Han Empire.

My Notes

_____

_____

_____

_____

_____

_____

_____

_____

_____

① **DESCRIBING** Use the web organizer below to show the ways Qin changed the life of early Chinese.

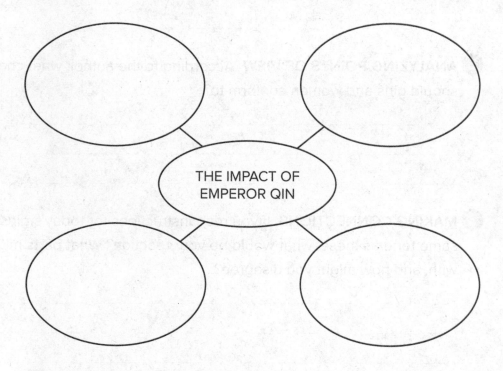

THE IMPACT OF EMPEROR QIN

② **IDENTIFYING CAUSE AND EFFECT** What caused the end of the Qin dynasty?

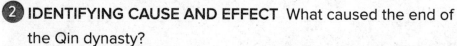

CAUSES	EFFECT
	THE END OF THE QIN DYNASTY

3 HISTORY How did land ownership change because of the increase in population during the Han rule?

_____

_____

_____

_____

_____

4 **ANALYZING EVENTS** Analyze the results of expanding trade and the development of the Silk Road during the Han dynasty. Use the organizer to support your analysis of the text.

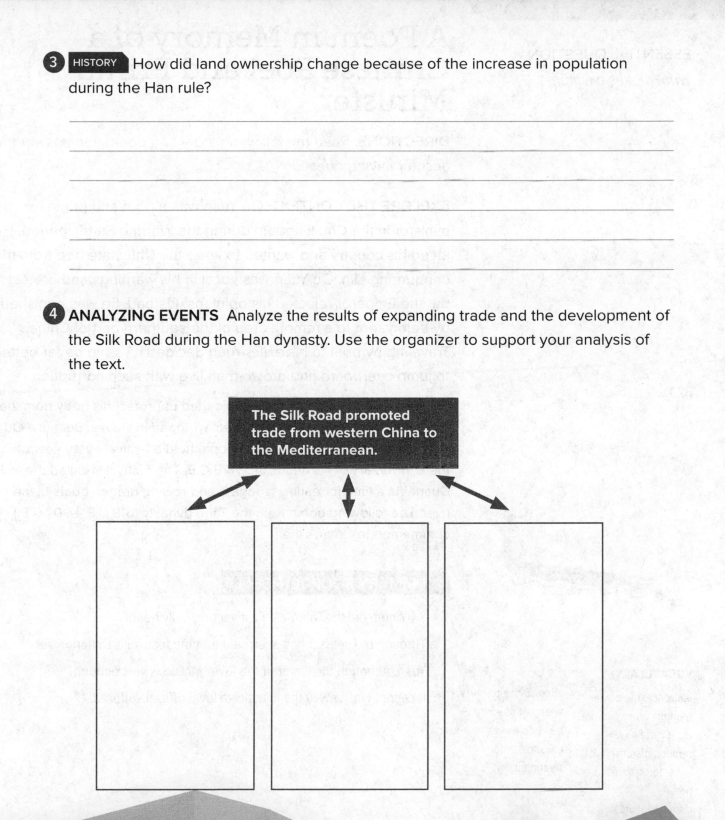

The Silk Road promoted trade from western China to the Mediterranean.

A Poem in Memory of a Chinese Poet and Prime Minister

ESSENTIAL QUESTION
What makes a culture unique?

DIRECTIONS: Read the following story and poem and answer the accompanying questions.

EXPLORE THE CONTEXT: Qu Yuan was a poet and prime minister in the Chu kingdom during the Warring States period. He loved his country and wanted to keep the Chu state free from the conquering Qin. Qu Yuan was vocal in his warnings and protests, but the Emperor rejected his opinions. Instead, he was punished by being sent to a remote area of the southern part of China. Traveling by boat to his exile, Yuan decided it would be far better to jump overboard and drown than live with such corruption.

While searching for Yuan, the people tried to protect his body from the fish by making "zong-zi," rice packets wrapped in leaves. Because Qu Yuan was so loved, the Chinese people hold a festival every year on the anniversary of his death, in 278 B.C.E. The festival is called the Duan Wu, a time for eating "zong-zi" and rowing dragon boats in the river. The following poem from the Tang dynasty (618 C.E.—907 C.E.) commemorates Yuan's life.

PRIMARY SOURCE: POEM

66 Whom did the Duan Wu Festival originally honor?
Through the years it has been said that the festival is to honor Qu Yuan. Although the water of the River Mi Luo is vast enough,
It cannot wash away the injustice a loyal official suffered. 99

VOCABULARY

influence: the power to make other persons act a certain way
remote: distant
exile: force to leave home
corruption: dishonest behavior for personal gain

zong-zi: rice packets wrapped often in bamboo leaves
injustice: unfair treatment

1 DETERMINING POINT OF VIEW Discuss with a partner the tone of this poem. Do you believe the writer wanted this poem to convey outrage, sympathy, sorrow, acceptance, or something else? Use evidence from the poem to support your answer.

_____

_____

_____

_____

2 DRAWING CONCLUSIONS What does this poem suggest about the ruling power, the Emperor of the Chu?

_____

_____

_____

_____

3 HISTORY What historic developments came after Qu Yuan's exile and death? Use Chapter 8, Lesson 3 to help you support your ideas about what occurred after the Period of the Warring States when Qu Yuan lived in the Chu kingdom.

_____

_____

_____

_____

4 CIVICS How did the Emperor's decision to exile Qu Yuan impact the people he ruled? Explain your answer with supporting details.

_____

_____

_____

_____

A Gateway from Han Dynasty (202 B.C.E.–220 C.E.)

DIRECTIONS: Study the image and answer the accompanying questions.

EXPLORE THE CONTEXT: This newly-built gateway is located near the original gateway to China's first Buddhist temple, built around 68 C.E. Gateways were built for both memorial and decorative purposes. Some were made of stone or brick, while others were constructed of wood. Often, they were marked with moral principles, achievements of a certain family's ancestors, or descriptions of government achievements. They were usually placed in front of a temple, a tomb, a bridge, or at the entrance to a city or an area within a city.

PRIMARY SOURCE: ARCHITECTURE

1 **DRAWING CONCLUSIONS** Why would the Chinese build such an elaborate and ornamental gateway? Cite text from Lesson 3.

_____

_____

_____

_____

2 **EVALUATING EVIDENCE** Evaluate what you observe in the image along with what you read in the text in Lesson 3 describing the growth of the Han Empire.

_____

_____

_____

_____

3 **COMPARING AND CONTRASTING** How does the gateway in the image compare with the Great Wall of China in appearance and purpose?

_____

_____

_____

_____

4 **INFERRING** Why might a government or group of people construct elaborate buildings?

_____

_____

_____

_____

ESSENTIAL QUESTION

What makes a culture unique?

❶ Think About It

Review the supporting questions you developed at the opening of the chapter. Review the evidence you found in Chapter 8. Were you able to answer each of your Supporting Questions?

If you didn't find enough evidence to answer your Supporting Questions, what do you think you need to consider?

_____

_____

_____

_____

❷ Organize Your Evidence

Use a chart like the one below to organize the evidence you will use to support your Position Statement.

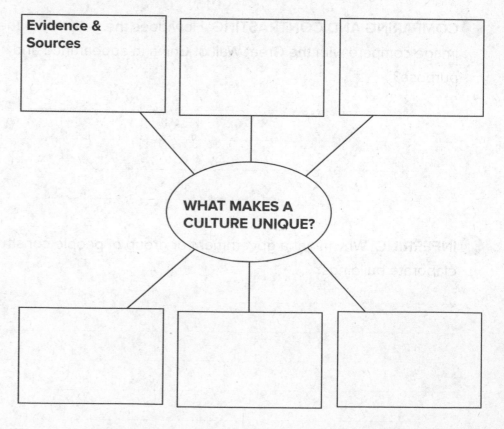

Evidence & Sources

WHAT MAKES A CULTURE UNIQUE?

③ Talk About It

Discuss your position statement and the evidence you have gathered with a small group or a partner. Check your group's understanding and answer any questions members may have. Consider any additional advice or input they may have.

④ Connect to the Essential Question

Create a slide show presentation that shows various influences that can lead to the creation of unique cultures. Use Chapter 8 lessons and Inquiry Journal sources to help you identify geographies, people, governments, military forces, ideas, and philosophies that can change how a culture takes shape. Show the effect of such influences on culture development.

CITIZENSHIP
TAKING ACTION

MAKE CONNECTIONS Culture includes many things, such as the beliefs, art, and customs of a group. It can include the way people worship, the movies they watch, and the music they listen to. It also can include the way they interact, such as at home, in school or at work, or through social media.

Many forces create the culture in which people live. It was true in early China as well as today in modern China. It is true of the ever-changing culture of America. Examine some of the influences that make our culture the way it is, and consider an element you feel strongly about. Are there some aspects of American culture you believe should change? If so, think about what kind of informed action on your part might help change them.

DIRECTIONS: Consider some way of thought, government action, or philosophy of life you believe would be positive for your culture. Research the topic you feel you could campaign for, and take your knowledge into the real world. Write an example of how you would promote this idea to your classmates, hoping to benefit American culture starting in your very own school.

_____

_____

_____

_____

_____

_____

_____

_____

Rome: Republic to Empire

ESSENTIAL QUESTION

How do governments change?

Think about how this question might relate to Rome as it changed from a republic to an empire.

TALK ABOUT IT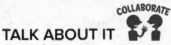

Discuss with a partner what type of information you would need to know to answer this question. For example, one question might be: *How do individuals change the way a government is run?*

DIRECTIONS: Now write down three additional questions that would help you explain how the Roman government changed over time.

MY RESEARCH QUESTIONS

Supporting Question 1:

_____

_____

Supporting Question 2:

_____

_____

Supporting Question 3:

_____

_____

The Founding of Rome

DIRECTIONS: Search for evidence in Chapter 9, Lesson 1 to help you answer the following questions.

1 HISTORY Fill in the chart below to describe two different legends about how Rome was founded.

Legends of Rome's Founding	
The Aeneid	
Romulus and Remus	

2 HISTORY Who were the Etruscans?

_____

_____

_____

_____

_____

_____

_____

ESSENTIAL QUESTION

How do governments change?

As you gather evidence to answer the Essential Question, think about:

- legends about Rome's founding.
- the influence of the Etruscans.
- how Rome changed after overthrowing Etruscan rule.

My Notes

_____

_____

_____

_____

_____

_____

_____

_____

3 EXPLAINING EFFECTS How did the Etruscans influence Roman culture?

_____

_____

_____

_____

_____

_____

_____

4 CONTRASTING How did the new Roman Republic differ from Rome under Etruscan rule?

_____

_____

_____

_____

_____

_____

_____

_____

5 EXPLAINING Why were the Romans able to rule effectively?

_____

_____

_____

_____

_____

How do governments change?

Etruscan Artwork

DIRECTIONS: Examine the image below and answer the accompanying questions.

EXPLORE THE CONTEXT: Like some other ancient cultures, the Etruscans had skilled artists. Etruscan artists painted tomb walls with many types of colorful images, such as the scene in the painting below created in the 500s B.C.E.

PRIMARY SOURCE: PAINTING

1A DESCRIBING Describe the scene shown in the image.

_____

_____

_____

_____

_____

_____

_____

_____

_____

_____

_____

_____

1B ANALYZING Why did the Etruscans most likely include these Images?

_____

_____

_____

_____

_____

_____

2 HISTORY Why might the Etruscans have created paintings on the walls of tombs?

_____

_____

_____

_____

_____

_____

Women in Etruscan Society

DIRECTIONS: Read the following excerpt and answer the accompanying questions.

EXPLORE THE CONTEXT: Various cultures across time have had different opinions of women and their place in society. Many cultures in the past viewed women as second-class citizens. In the excerpt below, the author writes about the Etruscans' view of women.

SECONDARY SOURCE: BOOK

66 No one of these is more conspicuous than the position assigned to woman in Etruscan civilization. It was in astonishing contrast to her place among the polished Greeks. . . . With the Etruscans, evidently a strictly monogamous people, she was the equal and the companion of her husband. She sat by his side at the feasting board, she was cared for in the most attentive manner, her image was carved with his on their common tomb, and there are a thousand evidences that she was not merely the idol, but the honored helpmate of the man. It was from this Etruscan example that early Rome drew the principle of monogamy and of the substantial independence of woman. 99

—from *The Ethnologic Affinities of the Ancient Etruscans*, 1889

VOCABULARY

conspicuous: obvious
evidently: clearly
monogamous: married to one person
attentive: thoughtfully helpful
helpmate: spouse, companion, helper, partner
substantial: sizeable, significant

1 EXPLAINING What were the Etruscans' views on marriage?

_____

_____

_____

_____

_____

2A **CONTRASTING** How did the Etruscans' views on women differ from those of many other cultures of the past?

_____

_____

_____

_____

_____

_____

2B **DESCRIBING** Describe how women were treated in Etruscan society.

_____

_____

_____

_____

_____

_____

_____

3 CIVICS How did the Etruscans' treatment of women affect Roman culture?

_____

_____

_____

_____

_____

_____

Rome as a Republic

DIRECTIONS: Search for evidence in Chapter 9, Lesson 2 to help you answer the following questions.

ESSENTIAL QUESTION

How do governments change?

As you gather evidence to answer the Essential Question, think about:

- the social structure of Rome.
- how Rome's government changed.
- how the Punic Wars extended Rome's territory and rule.

My Notes

_____

_____

_____

_____

_____

_____

_____

_____

1 CIVICS Use the chart to compare the lives of patricians and plebeians in Rome.

Patricians	Plebeians

2 **EXPLAINING** List the three branches of Roman government, and explain the function of each.

_____

_____

_____

_____

_____

_____

3 CIVICS How did the plebeians win their place in the Roman government?

_____

_____

_____

_____

4 HISTORY How did Rome gain control of Sicily?

_____

_____

_____

_____

_____

5 IDENTIFYING EFFECTS What was the effect on Rome of the Second Punic War?

_____

_____

_____

_____

_____

_____

6 RELATING EVENTS Why was the Third Punic War so significant?

_____

_____

_____

_____

Living Under Roman Laws

How do governments change?

DIRECTIONS: Read the following excerpt and answer the accompanying questions.

EXPLORE THE CONTEXT: The Roman justice system changed over time. One major change was posting the city's laws, known as the Twelve Tables, in the Forum for all to see. The Twelve Tables made up the first written code of law, drafted in 451 B.C.E. Below is an excerpt from Table VIII.

PRIMARY SOURCE: LEGAL CODE

❝**Table VIII. Torts or Delicts**

23. . . . Whoever is convicted of speaking false witness shall be flung from the Tarpeian Rock.

24a. If a weapon has sped accidentally from one's hand, rather than if one has aimed and hurled it, to atone for the deed a ram is substituted as a peace offering to prevent blood revenge.

24b. If anyone pastures on or cuts stealthily by night . . . another's crops . . . the penalty shall be capital punishment, and, after having been hung up, death as a sacrifice to Ceres, a punishment more severe than in homicide. ❞

—from *The Twelve Tables*, 451–450 B.C.E.

VOCABULARY

Torts: civil offenses or wrongdoings
Delicts: a civil crime requiring that money be paid
convicted: found guilty of a crime
atone: make amends

pastures on: to allow one's animals to graze upon
stealthily: in a sneaky manner
Ceres: the Roman Goddess of crops
homicide: murder

❶ ANALYZING What does the punishment for "speaking false witness" tell you about the Romans?

_____

_____

_____

_____

2A **CONTRASTING** Did the Romans make a distinction between causing accidental harm and causing deliberate harm to another person? How do you know this?

_____

_____

_____

_____

_____

2B **EXPLAINING** What does this distinction tell you about the Roman justice system?

_____

_____

_____

3A CIVICS What is the punishment for stealing crops or allowing one's animals to graze on another person's crops?

_____

_____

_____

_____

_____

3B **ANALYZING** Why do you think this penalty was "more severe than in homicide"?

_____

_____

_____

_____

Hannibal Wages War Against Rome

Copyright © McGraw-Hill Education; Polybius in Dana Carleton Munro. 1904. A Source Book of Roman History. Boston, USA. D.C. Heath & Co., Publishers.

ESSENTIAL QUESTION

How do governments change?

DIRECTIONS: Read the following excerpt and answer the accompanying questions.

EXPLORE THE CONTEXT: Polybius was a Greek historian and statesman who lived in Rome. He wrote many books about Rome and its development into a powerful, important entity. In the excerpt below, he writes about the actions of Hannibal, Carthage's greatest general.

PRIMARY SOURCE: BOOK

❝Passing the winter in the Celtic territory, Hannibal kept his Roman prisoners in close confinement, supplying them very sparingly with food; while he treated their allies with great kindness from the first, and finally called them together and addressed them, 'alleging that he had not come to fight against them, but against Rome in their behalf; and that, therefore, if they were wise, they would attach themselves to him: because he had come to restore freedom to the Italians, and to assist them to recover their cities and territory which they had severally lost to Rome.' With these words he dismissed them without ransom to their own homes, wishing by this policy to attract the inhabitants of Italy to his cause, and to alienate their affections from Rome, and to awaken the resentment of all those who considered themselves to have suffered by the loss of harbors or cities under the Roman rule. ❞

—from *Polybius, Book III, Chapter 77, Hannibal and the Punic Wars,* c. 200–118 B.C.E.

VOCABULARY

confinement: to be imprisoned

sparingly: in a poor or stingy way

alleging: claiming

severally: individually

alienate: to separate, to turn against

resentment: bitterness, anger, harsh feelings

1 **CONTRASTING** How did Hannibal's treatment of his prisoners differ?

_____

_____

_____

2 GEOGRAPHY Why might some Italians have resented Rome?

_____

_____

_____

_____

3 **EXPLAINING** What did Hannibal tell Rome's allies?

_____

_____

_____

_____

4 CIVICS Think about your responses to questions 2 and 3. Why did Hannibal behave this way?

_____

_____

_____

5 **DRAWING CONCLUSIONS** Which part of the excerpt leads you to that conclusion?

_____

_____

_____

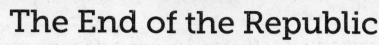

The End of the Republic

DIRECTIONS: Search for evidence in Chapter 9, Lesson 3 to help you answer the following questions.

1 EXPLAINING Explain the policy of "bread and circuses."

_____

_____

_____

_____

_____

2A CONTRASTING How were Tiberius and Gaius Gracchus different from many other Roman government officials?

_____

_____

_____

_____

_____

2B EXPLAINING EFFECTS What was the result of the brothers' actions?

_____

_____

_____

_____

_____

ESSENTIAL QUESTION

How do governments change?

As you gather evidence to answer the Essential Question, think about:

- how the poor were viewed by government officials.
- how powerful individuals changed the Roman government and people's lives.

My Notes

_____

_____

_____

_____

_____

_____

3 **CONTRASTING** Complete the Venn diagram to show similarities and differences between the generals Marius and Sulla.

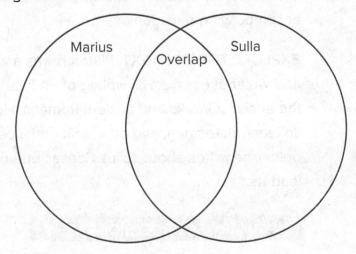

Marius   Overlap   Sulla

4 CIVICS How did Caesar's rise to power change Rome?

_____

_____

_____

5 HISTORY What was the relationship between Octavian and Antony? How did Antony's relationship with Cleopatra affect this relationship?

_____

_____

_____

_____

_____

6 CIVICS After Octavian assumed power, what was his opinion about Rome's republican form of government?

_____

_____

Plutarch on Julius Caesar's Rise to Power

ESSENTIAL QUESTION
How do governments change?

DIRECTIONS: Read the following excerpt and answer the accompanying questions.

EXPLORE THE CONTEXT: Plutarch was a well-known biographer and writer of essays. His writing often focused on the culture of the ancient Greeks and ancient Romans. He wrote biographies of soldiers, statesmen, and other influential people. In the excerpt below, he writes about Julius Caesar, one of Rome's most famous leaders.

PRIMARY SOURCE: BIOGRAPHY

   66 In his pleadings at Rome, his eloquence soon obtained him great credit and favor, and he won no less upon the affections of the people by the affability of his manners and address, in which he showed a tact and consideration beyond what could have been expected at his age; and the open house he kept, the entertainments he gave, and the general splendor of his manner of life contributed little by little to create and increase his political influence. His enemies slighted the growth of it at first, presuming it would soon fail when his money was gone; whilst in the meantime it was growing up and flourishing among the common people. . . . **99**

— Plutarch, *Life of Caesar*, c. 96–98 C.E.

VOCABULARY

pleadings: public statements

eloquence: a persuasive and forceful way of speaking or writing

favor: approval, support

affability: friendliness, pleasantness

tact: a thoughtful or polite way of doing something

slighted: ignored

flourishing: thriving

1A CIVICS Which quality did Caesar possess that made him popular with his peers in Rome?

_____

_____

_____

_____

1B IDENTIFYING Which quality did Caesar possess that made him popular with the common people of Rome?

_____

_____

2 INFERRING Consider your answers to questions 1A and 1B. Why were these qualities most likely important?

_____

_____

_____

_____

_____

_____

_____

_____

3 ANALYZING What does Plutarch mean when he says that Caesar "showed a tact and consideration beyond what could have been expected at his age"?

_____

_____

_____

4 EXPLAINING Why did Caesar's enemies think he would fail?

_____

_____

_____

_____

Plutarch on Julius Caesar's Rival, Pompey

DIRECTIONS: Read the following excerpt and answer the accompanying questions.

EXPLORE THE CONTEXT: In this excerpt, Plutarch writes about the Roman senator Pompey. Julius Caesar, another senator named Crassus, and Pompey made up the First Triumvirate, equally sharing power in Rome. However, Pompey later became Caesar's main rival.

PRIMARY SOURCE: BIOGRAPHY

66 Never had any Roman the people's good-will and devotion more zealously throughout all the changes of fortune, more early in its first springing up, or more steadily rising with his prosperity, or more constant in his adversity than Pompey had. . . . In Pompey there were many [causes] that helped to make him the object of their love; his temperance, his skill and exercise in war, his eloquence of speech, integrity of mind, and affability in conversation and address; insomuch that no man ever asked a favor with less offence, or conferred one with a better grace. When he gave, it was without assumption; when he received, it was with dignity and honor. 99

— Plutarch, *Life of Pompey*, 96–98 C.E.

VOCABULARY

zealously: eagerly, enthusiastically
prosperity: wealth
adversity: hardship, difficulty
affability: friendliness, pleasantness

temperance: restraint,
integrity: honesty, reliability
conferred: granted, presented

1 ANALYZING What does Plutarch mean when he says, "Never had any Roman the people's good-will and devotion more zealously throughout all the changes of fortune, more early in its first springing up, or more steadily rising with his prosperity, or more constant in his adversity than Pompey had?"

_____

_____

_____

2 **EXPLAINING** What might be another way of saying "When he gave, it was without assumption; when he received, it was with dignity and honor?"

_____

_____

_____

_____

_____

_____

_____

3 **CIVICS** Why did the Roman people love Pompey?

_____

_____

_____

_____

_____

_____

_____

4 **COMPARING** According to Plutarch, how were Pompey and Julius Caesar the same?

_____

_____

_____

_____

_____

_____

_____

ESSENTIAL QUESTION

How do governments change?

As you gather evidence to answer the Essential Question, think about:

- the effects that various rulers had on Rome.
- how the borders of the Roman Empire expanded.
- how the Roman economy changed over time.

My Notes

_____

_____

_____

_____

_____

_____

_____

_____

Rome Builds an Empire

DIRECTIONS: Search for evidence in Chapter 9, Lesson 4 to help you answer the following questions.

1 CIVICS Use the chart to describe reforms in Rome made by Caesar Augustus.

Caesar Augustus's Reforms	
Military	
Architecture	
Government	
Law	

2 EXPLAINING CAUSES Why did the Praetorian Guard execute Caligula?

_____

_____

_____

_____

3A **UNDERSTANDING CHRONOLOGY** Name the five "good emperors" in order of their reigns.

_____

_____

3B **CITING TEXT EVIDENCE** List at least one way that each of these emperors strengthened the Roman Empire.

_____

_____

_____

_____

_____

_____

_____

4 **IDENTIFYING** Where did the Roman Empire expand under Trajan's rule?

_____

_____

_____

_____

_____

5 **ECONOMICS** How did the Roman navy aid Rome's economy?

_____

_____

_____

Polybius on the Army of the Roman Empire

DIRECTIONS: Read the following excerpt and answer the accompanying questions.

EXPLORE THE CONTEXT: Greek historian Polybius had a great deal to say about Rome, including its army. In this excerpt, he gives his opinion about the soldiers' readiness for battle.

ESSENTIAL QUESTION

How do governments change?

VOCABULARY

flexible: able to change easily
equipped: ready, armed with weapons
moreover: in addition
detachment: a military unit that is separate from the main body of troops

maniple: a military unit of 60 or 120 soldiers
serviceable: working, functioning
flourishing: thriving

PRIMARY SOURCE: BOOK

❝"The Roman order on the other hand is flexible; for every Roman, once armed and on the field, is equally well equipped for every place, time, or appearance of the enemy. He is, moreover, quite ready and needs to make no change, whether he is required to fight in the main body, or in a detachment, or in a single maniple, or even by himself. Therefore, as the individual members of the Roman force are so much more serviceable, their plans are also much more often attended by success than those of others. . . .❞

— Polybius, *Book XVIII, Chapter 32, Flexibility of the Roman Order,* c. 200–118 B.C.E.

1 ANALYZING What is Polybius's opinion of the Roman army?

_____

_____

_____

_____

_____

_____

_____

2 **EXPLAINING** What does Polybius mean when he says that the soldiers need "to make no change, whether he is required to fight in the main body, or in a detachment, or in a single maniple, or even by himself?"

_____

_____

_____

_____

_____

_____

_____

3 **CIVICS** Why does Polybius believe that Roman soldiers often defeat their enemies?

_____

_____

_____

_____

_____

_____

_____

4 **INFERRING** Based on Polybius's statements, what quality are other armies lacking?

_____

_____

_____

_____

_____

_____

_____

Tacitus on the Emperor Nero

How do governments change?

DIRECTIONS: Read the following excerpt and answer the accompanying questions.

EXPLORE THE CONTEXT: Tacitus was a public official in Rome. In his book *Annals,* he wrote about the Roman Empire during 14 C.E. to 68 C.E. In this excerpt, he wrote about Nero, an emperor famous for being cruel.

VOCABULARY

fancy: liking, desire
chariot: similar to a carriage
degrading: shameful
theatrical: dramatic, as if on the stage

sacred: blessed
prophetic: able to see into the future
deity: a God or Goddess

PRIMARY SOURCE: BOOK

❝He [Nero] had long had a fancy for driving a four-horse chariot, and a no less degrading taste for singing to the harp, in a theatrical fashion, when he was at dinner. This, he would remind people, was a royal custom, and had been the practice of ancient chiefs; it was celebrated, too, in the praises of poets, and was meant to show honor to the gods. Songs indeed, he said, were sacred to Apollo, and it was in the dress of a singer that that great and prophetic deity was seen in Roman temples as well as in Greek cities. ❞

— Tacitus, *Annals,* Book XIV, Chapter 14, Nero's Amusements, c. 105–109 C.E.

1 ANALYZING Based on this passage, what do you think was Tacitus's opinion of Nero and his behavior?

_____

_____

_____

_____

_____

2 **INFERRING** Tacitus thinks Nero's "fancy for driving a four-horse chariot" shows a degrading, or shameful, taste. What action of Nero's does Tacitus think shows "a no less degrading taste"?

_____

_____

_____

_____

_____

3 **IDENTIFYING CAUSES** Why did Nero sing at dinner?

_____

_____

_____

_____

_____

_____

4 **HISTORY** How is the portrayal of Nero in this passage different from the description of Nero presented in your textbook?

_____

_____

_____

_____

_____

_____

1 Think About It

How do governments change?

Review the Supporting Questions that you developed at the beginning of the chapter. Review the evidence that you gathered in Chapter 9. Were you able to answer each Supporting Question?

If there was not enough evidence to answer your Supporting Questions, what additional evidence do you think you need?

_____

_____

_____

_____

2 Organize Your Evidence

Use the chart below to organize the evidence you will use to support your Position Statement.

Source of information	Specific Evidence to Cite From the Source	How does the evidence support my Position Statement?	How does this evidence connect to modern life?

3 Write About It

A position statement related to the Essential Question should reflect your conclusion about the evidence. Write a Position Statement for the ESSENTIAL QUESTION: *How do governments change?*

_____

_____

_____

_____

_____

_____

_____

_____

4 Connect to the Essential Question

On a separate piece of paper, create at least five good interview questions as if you were interviewing a person who lived during the rise of the Roman Empire. Think about asking what his or her life was like, how life was different under the republic, or how life changed under different emperors, etc.

After deciding what questions to ask, and using the Essential Question about how governments change as your central idea, write about how a person during the rise of the Roman Empire might have answered your questions.

CITIZENSHIP
TAKING ACTION

MAKE CONNECTIONS Think about how leaders in your local government commit themselves to helping your community. Is there more that you think these local leaders could do to help your community?

DIRECTIONS: Go online to find the names of the government officials who serve your town or county. Learn about their activities to help the people in your community. Then, start a petition or write a letter to the editor of your local newspaper on an issue you believe is not being addressed.

_____

_____

_____

_____

_____

_____

_____

_____

_____

_____

_____

_____

_____

_____

Roman Civilization

ESSENTIAL QUESTION

Why do civilizations rise and fall?

Think about how this question might relate to the way culture and civilizations are connected today.

TALK ABOUT IT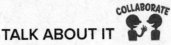

Discuss with a partner what type of information you would need to know to answer this question. For example, one question might be: *Where did Roman civilization come from?*

DIRECTIONS: Write three additional questions that would help you to explain why civilizations rise and fall.

MY RESEARCH QUESTIONS

Supporting Question 1:

_____

_____

Supporting Question 2:

_____

_____

Supporting Question 3:

_____

_____

The Roman Way of Life

DIRECTIONS: Search for evidence in Chapter 10, Lesson 1 to help you answer the following questions.

1 GEOGRAPHY How was Rome's location important for forming a new empire?

_____

_____

_____

2A **DESCRIBING** What was the Forum in Rome, and what happened there?

_____

_____

_____

2B **CITING TEXT EVIDENCE** How does the text describe the powerful role a father had in the typical Roman family?

_____

_____

_____

2C **DESCRIBING** What factors contributed to the changing status and role of women in Rome at this time?

_____

_____

_____

_____

_____

ESSENTIAL QUESTION
Why do civilizations rise and fall?

As you gather evidence to answer the Essential Question, think about:

- the characteristics of Roman civilization.
- the influences that shaped Roman civilization.

My Notes

3A EXPLAINING CAUSE AND EFFECT Discuss in pairs what changes occurred to the Roman people as its empire grew through its achievements in science and art. Fill in the graphic organizer to show specific examples of new ideas and advancements. Add more categories as you discuss the Romans' growing culture.

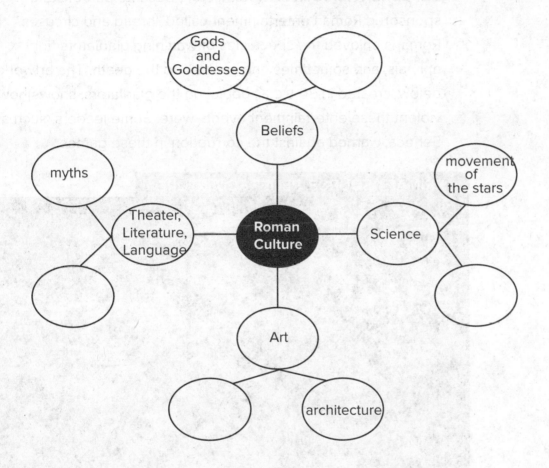

3B ANALYZING TEXT PRESENTATION The text states that the Romans "copied the Greeks in many ways but changed, or adapted, what they borrowed to match their own needs." Give two text examples showing ways the Romans borrowed from the Greeks and then changed it.

_____

_____

_____

_____

_____

Gladiators

DIRECTIONS: Examine the image below and answer the accompanying questions.

EXPLORE THE CONTEXT: Gladiators became part of state-sponsored Roman entertainment called "bread and circuses." Romans enjoyed the spectacles of watching gladiators fight animals, and sometimes one another, to the death. The artwork below, created in 30 B.C.E., depicting the gladiators, shows how violent these entertainment events were. Some leaders, such as Seneca, warned against the corruption in these games.

PRIMARY SOURCE: RELIEF SCULPTURE

1 INFERRING Why might these games have been appealing to many Romans?

_____

_____

_____

_____

2 IDENTIFYING CAUSES Why do you think gladiators often came from the poor population of Rome?

_____

_____

_____

_____

_____

3 MAKE CONNECTIONS Why might the gladiator Spartacus have led a slave rebellion? Cite details in the image and text from Lesson 1 to support your answer.

_____

_____

_____

_____

_____

_____

4 HISTORY How does this artwork contribute to today's knowledge of the Romans?

_____

_____

_____

The Pantheon

DIRECTIONS: Study the following image and answer the accompanying questions.

EXPLORE THE CONTEXT: The building in this photograph is the Roman Pantheon, which was built as a temple to honor Roman Gods. Its construction was completed in about 125 C.E. by the Emperor Hadrian. The Pantheon is made mostly of concrete and consists of two main parts: a porch supported by columns and a large, circular room with a great dome as its ceiling. This was the largest dome ever built until modern times. The Pantheon remains in good shape today, and for more than 1,000 years it has been used as a Christian church.

PRIMARY SOURCE: IMAGE

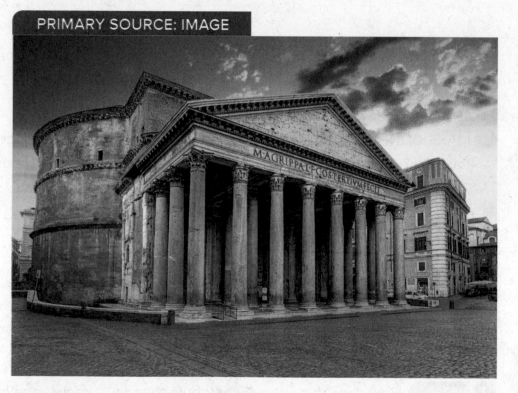

1 **DESCRIBING** What can you tell about the Pantheon from this photograph?

_____

_____

_____

_____

2 **DETERMINING CONTEXT** In what ways does this building demonstrate the influence of Greek culture on ancient Rome?

_____

_____

_____

_____

_____

_____

_____

_____

3 **EXPLAINING** That the Romans constructed this building using concrete?

_____

_____

_____

_____

_____

_____

_____

4 **DRAWING CONCLUSIONS** What conclusions can you draw about Roman architecture from this image of the Pantheon?

_____

_____

_____

_____

_____

_____

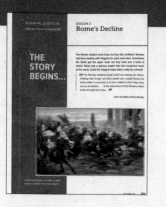

ESSENTIAL QUESTION

Why do civilizations rise and fall?

As you gather evidence to answer the Essential Question, think about:

- how the economic situation influenced the decline of Rome.
- what role emperors played in Rome's decline.

My Notes

_____

_____

_____

_____

_____

_____

_____

_____

Rome's Decline

DIRECTIONS: Search for evidence in Chapter 10, Lesson 2 to help you complete the following questions.

1A DETERMINING CENTRAL IDEAS What are two major issues that caused Rome to decline in the period 100 C.E. to 500 C.E.?

_____

_____

_____

_____

_____

_____

1B DESCRIBING Were Diocletian's reforms helpful in slowing Rome's decline?

_____

_____

_____

2 SUMMARIZING How did the rule of Emperors Diocletian, Constantine, and Theodosius lead to the separation of the Roman Empire into two empires?

_____

_____

_____

_____

_____

_____

3A IDENTIFYING EFFECTS The Romans let in the Visigoths and then treated them poorly. What effect did that treatment have on the Visigoths?

_____

_____

3B DESCRIBING How did attacks by the Vandals contribute to the weakening of Rome?

_____

_____

3C EXPLAINING CAUSE AND EFFECT What relationship did the later Roman Empire have with Germanic groups? How did this relationship help lead to the fall of Rome?

_____

_____

_____

_____

_____

4 SUMMARIZING Summarize in a few sentences which city led the Roman Empire when it was divided into two.

_____

_____

_____

_____

5 MAKING CONNECTIONS What are some examples of Rome's legacy to the modern world?

_____

_____

_____

Constantine

DIRECTIONS: Read the following excerpt and answer the accompanying questions.

EXPLORE THE CONTEXT: In 1776 C.E. English historian Edward Gibbon published the first volume of his most significant work, *The History of the Decline and Fall of the Roman Empire.* The six volumes of that work covered the empire's history from 98 C.E. to 1590 C.E. In this excerpt, Gibbon describes Constantine before he became Roman emperor.

SECONDARY SOURCE: BOOK

❝Instead of following [his father] Constantius in the West, he [Constantine] remained in the service of [Emperor] Diocletian, signalized his valor in the wars of Egypt and Persia, and gradually rose to the honorable station of a tribune of the first order. The figure of Constantine was tall and majestic; he was dexterous in all his exercises, intrepid in war, affable in peace; in his whole conduct, the active spirit of youth was tempered by habitual prudence; and while his mind was engrossed by ambition, he appeared cold and insensible to the allurements of pleasure. The favor of the people and soldiers, who had named him as a worthy candidate for the rank of Caesar, served only to exasperate the jealousy of [the Roman Emperor] Galerius. . . . Every hour increased the danger of Constantine, and the anxiety of his father, who, by repeated letters, expressed the warmest desire of embracing his son. ❞

— Edward Gibbon, *The History of The Decline and Fall of the Roman Empire*

VOCABULARY

intrepid: consistently courageous

affable: easy to be around or approach

dexterous: able to think or act skillfully

allurements: objects attracting desire

exasperate: to increase anger or impatience

1 IDENTIFYING Who did Constantine stay with when his father left for the West?

_____

_____

2 **IDENTIFYING CAUSES** What was the cause of Constantine's rise to tribune?

_____

_____

_____

_____

3 **INFERRING** Why did people and soldiers think Constantine would make a good emperor, or Caesar?

_____

_____

_____

_____

4 **MAKING CONNECTIONS** Would Constantine, as described in this excerpt, be as respected as a leader today as he was then?

_____

_____

_____

_____

5 **HISTORY** What effect might jealousy among the emperors, such as Galerius's jealousy of Constantine, have had on the Roman Empire?

_____

_____

_____

_____

How Alaric Captured Rome

DIRECTIONS: Read the following excerpt and answer the accompanying questions.

EXPLORE THE CONTEXT: Procopius, who lived and flourished during the years of about 490–560 C.E., wrote some of the most important sources on the Roman Empire and the Byzantine emperor Justinian. His work, *History of the Wars,* extended over eight books. This excerpt, taken from Books III and IV, describes the Vandalic War.

SECONDARY SOURCE: BOOK

66 [Alaric] chose out three hundred whom he knew to be of good birth and possessed of valour beyond their years, and told them secretly that he was about to make a present of them to certain of the patricians in Rome, pretending that they were slaves. And he instructed them that, as soon as they got inside the houses of those men, they should display much gentleness and moderation. . . . When all those who were to be their masters would most likely be already asleep after their meal, they should all come to the gate called Salarian and with a sudden rush kill the guards, who would have no previous knowledge of the plot, and open the gates as quickly as possible.

After making this declaration and sending the youths not long afterwards, he commanded the barbarians to make preparations for the departure, and he let this be known to the Romans. . . . And all the youths at the time of the day agreed upon came to this gate, and, assailing the guards suddenly, put them to death; then they opened the gates and received Alaric and the army into the city at their leisure. And they set fire to the houses which were next to the gate, among which was also the house of Sallust, who in ancient times wrote the history of the Romans, and the greater part of this house has stood half-burned up to my time; and after plundering the whole city and destroying the most of the Romans, they moved on. At that

VOCABULARY

assailing: attacking
plundering: stealing
perished: died or disappeared

1 ANALYZING What tone does the author's first sentence convey in this excerpt?

_____

_____

_____

_____

_____

_____

. . . continued

time they say that the Emperor Honorius in Ravenna received the
message from one of the eunuchs, evidently a keeper of the poultry, that
Rome had perished. And he cried out and said, 'And yet it has just eaten
from my hands!' . . . The eunuch comprehending his words said that it
was the city of Rome which had perished at the hands of Alaric. . . . **"**

— Procopius, *The Vandalic War,* c. 550 C.E.

2 CITING TEXT EVIDENCE How does the author show that Alaric made
use of the element of surprise in his attack on Roman leaders?

_____

_____

_____

_____

3 INFERRING Rome fell in 476 C.E. What detail in the excerpt suggests
that Rome struggled to recover after Alaric's attack?

_____

_____

_____

_____

4 ASSESSING CREDIBILITY Is this source a reliable account of the fall of
Rome? Why or why not?

_____

_____

_____

_____

ESSENTIAL QUESTION

Why do civilizations rise and fall?

As you gather evidence to answer the Essential Question, think about:

- how and why Constantinople became the "new Rome."

- how Byzantine civilization developed.

My Notes

_____

_____

_____

_____

_____

_____

_____

_____

_____

_____

The Byzantine Empire

DIRECTIONS: Search for evidence in Chapter 10, Lesson 3 to help you complete the following items.

1A **DRAWING CONCLUSIONS** How did Constantinople's location contribute to the initial success of the Byzantine Empire?

_____

_____

_____

_____

_____

1B **IDENTIFYING CAUSES** At first, Constantinople was known as "The New Rome," but over time it developed its own character. What caused this change?

_____

_____

_____

_____

_____

2A **EXPLAINING** What responsibilities did Justinian have as ruler of the Byzantine Empire?

_____

_____

_____

_____

2B CITING TEXT EVIDENCE What aspects of civil society are evident in the way Justinian and Theodora cooperated in their government? Find an example in the text to support Justinian and Theodora's actions.

_____

_____

_____

_____

3 ANALYZING TEXT PRESENTATION What might the historian, Procopius, have meant when he reported Theodora's words of warning to Justinian?

_____

_____

_____

_____

4 HISTORY What events or actions were important to Justinian's legacy? Choose the three actions you think are most important and record them in the graphic organizer.

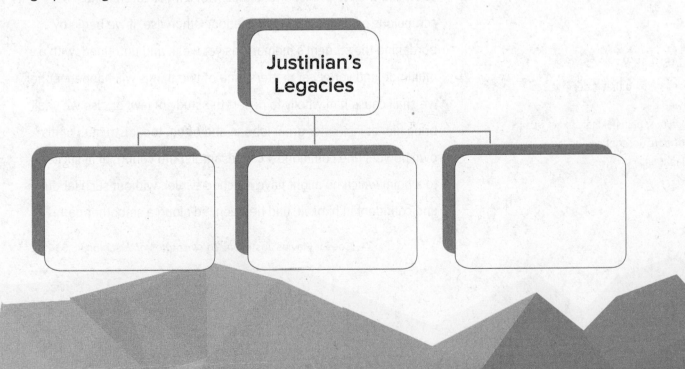

Justinian's Legacies

Justice and Law

ESSENTIAL QUESTION
Why do civilizations rise and fall?

DIRECTIONS: Read the excerpt and answer the accompanying questions.

EXPLORE THE CONTEXT: The Justinian Code is a collection of laws and legal interpretations created by a group of legal scholars under the direction of the Byzantine emperor Justinian, who ruled from 527 C.E. to 565 C.E. This code became the basis for legal systems in most of the Western countries for centuries.

PRIMARY SOURCE: LEGAL CODE

❝Justice is the set and constant purpose which gives to every man his due.

1 Jurisprudence is the knowledge of things divine and human, the science of the just and the unjust.

2 Having laid down these general definitions, and our object being the exposition of the law of the Roman people, we think that the most advantageous plan will be to commence with an easy and simple path, and then to proceed to details with a most careful and scrupulous exactness of interpretation. Otherwise, if we begin by burdening the student's memory, as yet weak and untrained, with a multitude and variety of matters, one of two things will happen: either we shall cause him wholly to desert the study of law, or else we shall bring him at last, after great labour, and often, too, distrustful of his own powers (the commonest cause, among the young, of ill-success), to a point which he might have reached earlier, without such labour and confident in himself, had he been led along a smoother path.❞

— Caesar Flavius Justinian, *The Institutes of Justinian,* c. 534 C.E.

VOCABULARY

due: something that is deserved or owed
scrupulous: painstakingly exact
exposition: description and explanation

1 **DETERMINING MEANING** The author writes that the purpose of the work is "the exposition of the law of the Roman people." What is the meaning of that phrase?

_____

_____

_____

2 **SUMMARIZING** What process does the Code recommend for studying the law? Why?

_____

_____

_____

_____

_____

3 HISTORY What can you infer about the nature of Roman law based on this advice?

_____

_____

_____

4 **MAKING CONNECTIONS** Do you think the Justinian Code's statement "Justice is the set and constant purpose which gives to every man his due" is true today? Why or why not?

_____

_____

_____

5 **INFERRING** How does a legal system contribute to the development of a civilization?

_____

_____

_____

Byzantine Mosaics

DIRECTIONS: Examine the following image and answer the accompanying questions.

EXPLORE THE CONTEXT: Mosaics are part of the artistic legacy left by the Byzantine Empire. Mosaics like the one below created around the mid-500s C.E., used geometric patterns and often included images of daily life or images of religious figures.

PRIMARY SOURCE: MOSAICS

1 **DESCRIBING** What does this mosaic show about life in the Byzantine Empire?

_____

_____

_____

_____

_____

2 ECONOMICS What does the mosaic tell you about the Byzantine economy?

_____

_____

_____

_____

_____

_____

_____

3 **ASKING QUESTIONS** What questions could you ask to guide you to learn more about this mosaic?

_____

_____

_____

_____

_____

_____

4 **MAKING CONNECTIONS** What kinds of art would future historians need to study to learn about daily life in the 2000s C.E.?

_____

_____

_____

_____

_____

_____

ESSENTIAL QUESTION

Why do civilizations rise and fall?

1 Think About It

Review the supporting questions that you developed at the beginning of the chapter. Review the evidence that you gathered in Chapter 10. Were you able to answer each Supporting Question?

If there was not enough evidence to answer your Supporting Questions, what additional evidence do you think you need to consider?

_____

_____

_____

2 Organize Your Evidence

Use a chart like the one below to organize the evidence you will use to support your Position Statement. Think about the two empires you read about: the Roman Empire and the Byzantine Empire. What were the reasons for each empire's rise? What contributed to each empire's decline?

Fill in the chart with details from Chapter 10.

	Roman Empire	Byzantine Empire
Rise		
Fall		

③ Write About It

Write a Position Statement for the ESSENTIAL QUESTION: *Why do civilizations rise and fall?* A position statement related to the Essential Question should reflect your conclusion about the evidence.

_____

_____

_____

_____

_____

_____

_____

_____

_____

④ Talk About It

Work in small groups to discuss your findings about the rise and fall of civilizations. Use the feedback from your classmates before you write a summary statement. You may choose to refine your position statement after you have discussed it with your classmates. Group members should listen to each other's arguments, ask questions, and offer constructive advice.

⑤ Connect to the Essential Question

On a separate piece of paper or using a computer, create a graphic that explains the factors that contribute to the rise and fall of civilizations. The graphic should combine visual and text elements and reflect the evidence you've collected about the Roman and Byzantine Empires.

CITIZENSHIP
TAKING ACTION

MAKE CONNECTIONS Both the Roman Empire and the Byzantine Empire valued the rule of law. The rule of law means that a nation is governed by its legal code, and even a nation's leaders are expected to obey the law. The United States shares this value.

DIRECTIONS: With a partner or small group, create a public service announcement (PSA) explaining the importance of the rule of law. Perform your PSA as a skit or record it as a video and play it for your classmates.

_____

_____

_____

_____

_____

_____

_____

_____

_____

_____

_____

_____

_____

_____

_____

The Rise of Christianity

ESSENTIAL QUESTION

How do new ideas change the way people live?

Think about how this question might connect the practices important to early Christians with the practices of Christians today.

TALK ABOUT IT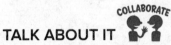

COLLABORATE

Discuss with a partner what type of information you would need to know to answer this question. For example, one question might be: How does understanding the ideas important in early Christianity relate to the ideas emphasized in different branches of modern Christianity?

DIRECTIONS: Now write down three additional questions you need to answer to explain how the practices of early Christians relate to Christianity today.

MY RESEARCH QUESTIONS

Supporting Question 1:

_____

_____

Supporting Question 2:

_____

_____

Supporting Question 3:

_____

_____

Early Christianity

DIRECTIONS: Search for evidence in Chapter 11, Lesson 1 to help you answer the following questions.

ESSENTIAL QUESTION

How do new ideas change the way people live?

As you gather evidence to answer the Essential Question, think about:

- the conflict between the Roman Empire and the Jewish people.
- the differences between Jewish practices and early Christian practices.

1 ANALYZING How did the Romans rule the Jewish people? What was the outcome of these methods?

_____

_____

_____

_____

_____

2 CULTURE In the graphic organizer below, write a summary of each of Jesus' parables. Then describe the lesson he was trying to teach his followers with each parable.

Parable	Lesson for Followers
The Good Samaritan	
The Prodigal Son	

My Notes

_____

_____

_____

_____

_____

_____

_____

3 **DESCRIBING** In the graphic organizer below, choose two Beatitudes and copy them into the first column. Then describe how each Beatitude can be interpreted in everyday language.

Beatitude	Interpretation

4 **IDENTIFYING CAUSES** Why do you think the Roman governor sentenced Jesus to death?

_____

_____

_____

_____

5 **ANALYZING INFORMATION** How did the apostles contribute to the early growth of Christianity?

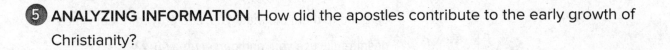

_____

_____

_____

_____

Jesus of Nazareth: Love Your Enemies

ESSENTIAL QUESTION

How do new ideas change the way people live?

VOCABULARY

twain: two
despitefully: in spite
persecute: continually harm

DIRECTIONS: Read the following excerpt and answer the accompanying questions.

EXPLORE THE CONTEXT: Unlike many early thinkers and philosophers, Jesus of Nazareth had different ideas about how to respond to persecution. In a violent time, he advocated for nonviolent means of interaction with those who would bring harm. The selection below was written by one of Jesus' apostles, Matthew.

PRIMARY SOURCE: HOLY BOOK

❝38 Ye have heard that it hath been said, An eye for an eye, and a tooth for a tooth:

39 But I say unto you, That ye resist not evil: but whosoever shall smite thee on thy right cheek, turn to him the other also.

40 And if any man will sue thee at the law, and take away thy coat, let him have thy cloak also.

41 And whosoever shall compel thee to go a mile, go with him twain.

42 Give to him that asketh thee, and from him that would borrow of thee turn not thou away.

43 Ye have heard that it hath been said, Thou shalt love thy neighbour, and hate thine enemy.

44 But I say unto you, Love your enemies, bless them that curse you, do good to them that hate you, and pray for them which despitefully use you, and persecute you. ❞

—from *The Holy Bible,* King James Version, Matthew 5:38–44

1 INFERRING Matthew writes that Jesus of Nazareth tells his followers to turn the other cheek. What does Jesus mean by this phrase?

_____

_____

2 ANALYZING INFORMATION Which two verses tell followers to give up material things to people who ask for them? What is the underlying reason for this generosity?

_____

_____

_____

_____

_____

3 EVALUATING EVIDENCE What evidence in the text can you find for a departure from Jewish scripture? How does Jesus turn away from these rules in his recommendations to followers?

_____

_____

_____

_____

4 ANALYZING How might these ideas have helped people who were poor or people who were suffering? Why did people believe what Jesus said?

_____

_____

_____

_____

The Epistle of Paul to the Romans

Copyright © McGraw-Hill Education; Romans 8:28-31, 38-39. The Holy Bible: King James Version.

ESSENTIAL QUESTION

How do new ideas change the way people live?

VOCABULARY

foreknow: know ahead of time
predestinate: decide a person's destiny before he or she is born
brethren: brothers

DIRECTIONS: Read the following excerpt and answer the accompanying questions.

EXPLORE THE CONTEXT: Saul did not support Christianity and was on his way to Damascus to arrest followers of Jesus. According to Christian teaching, while traveling there, Saul was blinded by a bright light. He then heard a voice asking him why he was determined to persecute Jesus. After having this vision, Saul converted to Christianity and became Paul the Apostle. From this point he dedicated himself to sharing Christianity with others through journeys, preaching, and through letters. Paul was named a saint by the Church after his death. In this letter to believers of Christ who lived in Rome, Paul writes about those who love God.

PRIMARY SOURCE: HOLY BOOK

❝28 And we know that all things work together for good to them that love God, to them who are called according to his purpose.

29 For whom he did foreknow, he also did predestinate to be conformed to the image of his Son, that he might be the firstborn among many brethren.

30 Moreover whom he did predestinate, them he also called: and whom he called, them he also justified: and whom he justified, them he also glorified.

31 What shall we then say to these things? If God be for us, who can be against us? . . .

38 For I am persuaded, that neither death, nor life, nor angels, nor principalities, nor powers, nor things present, nor things to come,

39 Nor height, nor depth, nor any other creature, shall be able to separate us from the love of God, which is in Christ Jesus our Lord. ❞

—from *The Holy Bible,* King James Version, Romans 8:28–31, 38–39

1 IDENTIFYING In the first line of the excerpt, for whom does Paul say that "all things work together for good"?

_____

_____

_____

2 INFERRING In the excerpt, what do you think Paul means by "If God be for us, who can be against us?"

_____

_____

_____

_____

3 IDENTIFYING Paul writes that nothing can separate believers "from the love of God, which is in Christ Jesus our Lord." What things does Paul list that cannot separate believers from the love of God?

_____

_____

_____

_____

4 ANALYZING Why do you think Paul wrote this letter to believers of Jesus who lived in Rome? Use what you have learned from Explore the Context as well as the passage.

_____

_____

_____

_____

ESSENTIAL QUESTION

*How do new ideas change
the way people live?*

As you gather evidence to answer the
Essential Question, think about:

- how the early Christian community
  was different from non-Christian
  communities in the Roman Empire.

- how the early Christian community
  spread its message.

My Notes

_____

_____

_____

_____

_____

_____

_____

_____

The Early Church

DIRECTIONS: Search for evidence in Chapter 11, Lesson 2 to help
you answer the following questions.

1 CIVICS In the graphic organizer below, write three ways in
which early Christian communities differed from other
communities that followed the ancient Roman religion.

Roman Empire's Religion	Christianity

2 ANALYZING EVENTS How did the Romans treat the early
Christians? How did that treatment affect the growth of
Christianity?

_____

_____

_____

ANALYZING EVENTS What did Constantine do to change the empire's position on Christianity? What effect did it have on the religion?

_____

_____

_____

_____

_____

_____

4 ECONOMICS How did Christianity spread into East Africa?

_____

_____

_____

_____

_____

_____

_____

_____

 EXPLAINING Why did early Christians eventually organize the church as a hierarchy?

_____

_____

_____

_____

_____

_____

Second Letter from Paul to Timothy

ESSENTIAL QUESTION

How do new ideas change the way people live?

DIRECTIONS: Read the following excerpt and answer the accompanying questions.

EXPLORE THE CONTEXT: In his second letter to the apostle Timothy, the apostle Paul explains how to spread the teachings of Christianity to nonbelievers. He tells Timothy to evangelize by explaining how any other way of life will lead people astray and increase their suffering.

VOCABULARY

reprove: scold
rebuke: criticize
exhort: urge
doctrine: set of beliefs or stated principles

PRIMARY SOURCE: HOLY BOOK

"1 I charge thee therefore before God, and the Lord Jesus Christ, who shall judge the quick and the dead at his appearing and his kingdom;

2 Preach the word; be instant in season, out of season; reprove, rebuke, exhort with all longsuffering and doctrine.

3 For the time will come when they will not endure sound doctrine; but after their own lusts shall they heap to themselves teachers, having itching ears;

4 And they shall turn away their ears from the truth, and shall be turned unto fables.

5 But watch thou in all things, endure afflictions, do the work of an evangelist, make full proof of thy ministry."

—from *The Holy Bible,* King James Version, 2 Timothy 4:1–5

1 INFERRING Based on the nature of these verses, what do you think Timothy is being instructed to do?

_____

_____

_____

_____

2 DESCRIBING According to this letter, what duty does an evangelist have?

_____

_____

_____

_____

_____

_____

3 EVALUATING EVIDENCE What evidence in the text can you find for Paul's worry that Christianity will not survive?

_____

_____

_____

_____

_____

_____

4 ANALYZING Based on the text, does Paul expect Timothy's task to be easy?

_____

_____

_____

Tertullian's Apology

Copyright © McGraw-Hill Education; Tertullian; Tertullian. Edited by Allan Menzies, DD. The Writings Of The Fathers Down To A.D. 325. Ante-Nicene Fathers - Volume 3. The Apology. Grand Rapids, Michigan: Wm. B. Eerdmans Publishing Company.

ESSENTIAL QUESTION

How do new ideas change the way people live?

DIRECTIONS: Read the following excerpt and answer the accompanying questions.

EXPLORE THE CONTEXT: This passage is from Tertullian, one of the teachers in the early Christian church. This style of writing is called an "apology." An apology in this style is not meant to apologize for a wrong done, but is meant to be a defense of something. In this case, it is Christianity. Here Tertullian explains to the Roman rulers the reasons why they should not hate Christians. When Tertullian wrote this piece, the rulers of the Roman Empire were against Christianity because they saw it as a threat to their power.

VOCABULARY

severities: actions that are severe
aggravates: makes worse
enmity: hatred

PRIMARY SOURCE: BOOK

❝Rulers of the Roman Empire, . . . if in this case alone you are afraid or ashamed to exercise your authority in making public inquiry with the carefulness which becomes justice; if, finally, the extreme severities inflicted on our people . . . stand in the way of our being permitted to defend ourselves before you, you cannot surely forbid the Truth to reach your ears by the secret pathway of a noiseless book. . . . We lay this before you as the first ground on which we urge that your hatred to the name of Christian is unjust. And the very reason which seems to excuse this injustice (I mean ignorance) at once aggravates and convicts it. For what is there more unfair than to hate a thing of which you know nothing[?] . . . The proof of their ignorance, at once condemning and excusing their injustice, is this, that those who once hated Christianity because they knew nothing about it, no sooner come to know it than they all lay down at once their enmity. From being its haters they become its disciples.❞

—from *The Apology,* by Tertullian, c. 197 C.E.

1 **EXPLAINING** How does this text explain that the Roman hatred of Christians is unjust?

_____

_____

_____

2 **ANALYZING** What is Tertullian offering to the Romans, and what does he want them to do with it?

_____

_____

_____

_____

_____

3 **SUMMARIZING** What is the lesson that the author is trying to teach?

_____

_____

_____

_____

4 **COMPARING** How is this passage similar to Paul's letter to Timothy?

_____

_____

_____

_____

ESSENTIAL QUESTION

How do new ideas change the way people live?

As you gather evidence to answer the Essential Question, think about:

- how the church established its authority in Rome.
- why the church eventually split into two factions.

My Notes

_____

_____

_____

_____

_____

_____

_____

_____

A Christian Europe

DIRECTIONS: Search for evidence in Chapter 11, Lesson 3 to help you answer the following questions.

1 ANALYZING IDEAS How were the ideas of church organization different in the eastern church compared to the western church?

_____

_____

_____

_____

_____

_____

2 DESCRIBING How did the Benedictine rule bring the teachings of Jesus into the lives of monks?

_____

_____

_____

_____

3 ANALYZING EVENTS What did Pope Gregory I do to encourage the spread of Christianity? Did it work and, if so, how?

_____

_____

_____

_____

_____

4 COMPARING AND CONTRASTING In the graphic organizer below, write the
similarities and differences between Pope Gregory I and Constantine.

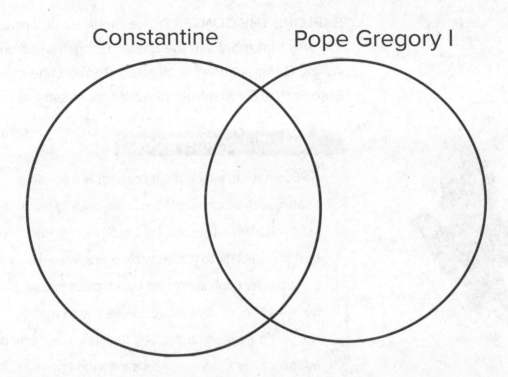

Constantine   Pope Gregory I

5 DESCRIBING In the graphic organizer below, describe missionaries and their
methods in early Christianity. Then describe how missionaries work today.

Early Christian Missionaries	Modern Christian Missionaries

The Monk at Prayer

Copyright © McGraw-Hill Education; Morison, E. F. 1912. St. Basil And His Rule: A Study In Early Monasticism. London, Edinburgh, New York, Toronto, Melbourne, and Bombay: Henry Frowde Oxford University Press.

ESSENTIAL QUESTION
How do new ideas change the way people live?

DIRECTIONS: Read the following excerpt and answer the accompanying questions.

EXPLORE THE CONTEXT: The monk Basil formed the basis for the way that monks in the Eastern Christian Church live and pray. As the Benedictine rule directed Benedictine monks in Western Europe, the Basilian rule directed monks in Eastern Europe.

PRIMARY SOURCE: BOOK

66 Ought we to pray without ceasing? Is it possible to obey such a command? These are questions which I see you are ready to ask. I will endeavor, to the best of my ability, to prove my case. Prayer is a petition for good addressed by the pious to God. But we do not rigidly confine our petition to words. Nor yet do we imagine that God requires to be reminded by speech. He knows our needs even though we do not ask Him. . . .

Thus mayest thou pray without ceasing, not in words, but by the whole conduct of thy life, so uniting thyself to God that thy life is one long, unceasing prayer. **99**

— Basil, *Homilies*, c. 306 C.E.

VOCABULARY

endeavor: attempt
pious: religious, obedient
unceasing: continuous, never-ending

1 INFERRING What does Basil mean when he says that God does not need to hear words?

_____

_____

_____

_____

2 IDENTIFYING What word does Basil use to describe the way that monks should pray, and what does it mean?

_____

_____

_____

_____

_____

3 EVALUATING EVIDENCE What evidence in the text can you find for the idea that God requires monks to do what they are told and follow certain rules?

_____

_____

_____

_____

_____

_____

_____

4 ANALYZING How does this text explain the connection between monks and the public?

_____

_____

_____

_____

_____

_____

Exposition of the Present State of the Churches

ESSENTIAL QUESTION

How do new ideas change the way people live?

DIRECTIONS: Read the following excerpt and answer the accompanying questions.

EXPLORE THE CONTEXT: In this text, Basil explains the animosity between each of the factions of Christianity as the western and eastern churches experience a painful split.

VOCABULARY

fleets: groups of ships

tempest: storm

watchwords: guiding principles

PRIMARY SOURCE: BOOK

❝To what then shall I liken our present condition? It may be compared, I think, to some naval battle which has arisen out of time old quarrels, and is fought by men who cherish a deadly hate against one another, of long experience in naval warfare, and eager for the fight. Look, I beg you, at the picture thus raised before your eyes. See the rival fleets rushing in dread array to the attack. With a burst of uncontrollable fury they engage and fight it out. Fancy, if you like, the ships driven to and fro by a raging tempest, while thick darkness falls from the clouds and blackens all the scenes so that watchwords are indistinguishable in the confusion, and all distinction between friend and foe is lost. . . . Jealousy of authority and the lust of individual mastery splits the sailors into parties which deal mutual death to one another. . . . They do not cease from their struggle each to get the better of the other, while their ship is actually settling down into the deep.❞

— Basil, *De Spiritu Sancto (The Book Of Saint Basil On The Spirit),*
c. 375 C.E.

1 INFERRING What does the writer of this document mean by "all distinction between friend and foe is lost"?

_____

_____

_____

_____

2 DESCRIBING How does this document describe the argument between the two church factions?

_____

_____

_____

_____

3 EVALUATING EVIDENCE What evidence in the text can you find for the reasons that Basil thinks the churches are fighting?

_____

_____

_____

_____

_____

4 ANALYZING How does Basil make arguments that are similar to the teachings of Jesus?

_____

_____

_____

_____

ESSENTIAL QUESTION

How do new ideas change the way people live?

① Think About It

Review the supporting questions that you developed at the beginning of the chapter. Review the evidence that you gathered in Chapter 11. Were you able to answer each Supporting Question? If there was not enough evidence to answer your Supporting Questions, what additional evidence do you think you need to consider?

_____

_____

② Organize Your Evidence

Use a chart such as the one below to organize the evidence you will use to support your Position Statement.

Source of information	Specific Evidence to Cite from the source	How Does the Evidence Support my Position Statement?

3 Write About It

A position statement related to the Essential Question should reflect your conclusion about the evidence. Write a Position Statement for the ESSENTIAL QUESTION: *How do new ideas change the way people live?*

_____

_____

_____

4 Talk About It

Work in a small group to present your position statement and evidence. Gather feedback from your classmates before you write your final conclusion. You may choose to refine your Position Statement after you have discussed it with your classmates. Group members should listen to each other's arguments, ask questions, and offer constructive feedback to help create clear Position Statements.

_____

_____

_____

5 Connect to the Essential Question

Create a poster comparing and contrasting how people in Europe and other parts of the Roman Empire lived before and after the birth of Christianity to answer the ESSENTIAL QUESTION: *How do new ideas change the way people live?*

_____

_____

_____

CITIZENSHIP
TAKING ACTION

MAKE CONNECTIONS Christianity spread across the Roman Empire because the empire's road network made it easy for Christians to travel and spread their message. Today, we do not need roads to help us communicate ideas across long distances. We have technology that can do that for us.

DIRECTIONS: Imagine you have a new idea that might improve your community. How would you spread that message? Write a 3–5 step plan to share your idea. Include which technologies or social media platforms you would use, how you would use each one, and why.

_____

_____

_____

_____

_____

_____

_____

_____

_____

_____

_____

_____

The Americas

ESSENTIAL QUESTION

What makes a culture unique?

Think about how this question might relate to the early cultures of the Americas.

TALK ABOUT IT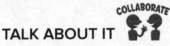

Discuss with a partner what type of information you would need to know to answer this question. For example, one question might be: How does geography help you understand the cultures of early Americans?

DIRECTIONS: Now write down three additional questions that would help you explain the parts of society that make a culture unique.

MY RESEARCH QUESTIONS

Supporting Question 1:

_____

_____

Supporting Question 2:

_____

_____

Supporting Question 3:

_____

_____

The First Americans

DIRECTIONS: Search for evidence in Chapter 12, Lesson 1 to help you answer the following questions.

ESSENTIAL QUESTION

What makes a culture unique?

As you gather evidence to answer the Essential Question, think about:

- how the land and geography of the Americas influenced the way people lived.
- the hunter-gatherer lifestyle and the emergence of agriculture.
- the evidence found of the earliest American societies.

1 **DETERMINING CENTRAL IDEAS** Use the web organizer below to take notes about the different types of geographical formations of the Americas.

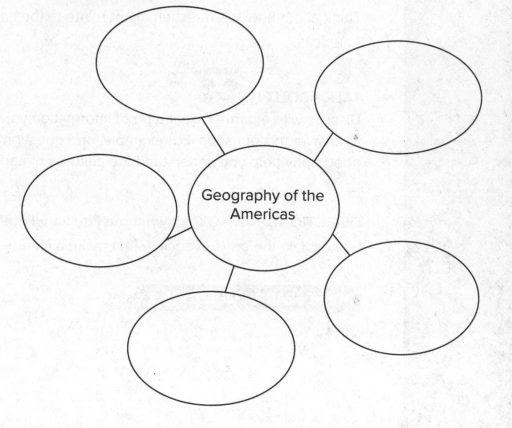

Geography of the Americas

2 **DIFFERENTIATING** Early Americans were hunter-gatherers and later began to farm the land. How are hunter-gatherers different from farmers?

_____

_____

_____

_____

_____

My Notes

_____

_____

_____

_____

_____

_____

_____

_____

3 SEQUENCING Using the information in the text, place the early Mesoamerican and South American cultures in chronological order on a time line in the space below.

4 DETERMINING CENTRAL IDEAS Use the graphic organizer below to take notes on the early cultures of North America. Record details about where and when each culture developed and how its people lived.

Culture	Location	When the culture thrived	Lifestyle
Hohokam			
Anasazi			
Mound Builders			
Mississippians			

Tools of the Early Americans

DIRECTIONS: Examine the image below and answer the accompanying questions.

EXPLORE THE CONTEXT: This image shows an assortment of ancient harpoons from Hog Island, Alaska. These tools were created thousands of years ago.

PRIMARY SOURCE: ARTIFACT

 GEOGRAPHY What can you tell about the natural resources of the early Americas from the artifact?

_____

_____

_____

_____

_____

_____

2 DETERMINING CONTEXT What type of technology would have been needed to make the artifact? How does this help you understand early American culture?

_____

_____

_____

_____

_____

_____

_____

3 INFERRING Look carefully at the tool. What can you infer about the culture from the designs?

_____

_____

_____

_____

_____

_____

_____

4 DRAWING CONCLUSIONS What conclusions can you draw about the type of food the society that created this artifact ate?

_____

_____

_____

_____

_____

_____

Inca Prayer

Copyright © McGraw-Hill Education: Means, Philip Ainsworth. 1931. Three Inca Prayers from Ancient Civilizations Of The Andes - Pages 437-439. New York: Charles Scribner's Sons.

ESSENTIAL QUESTION
What makes a culture unique?

DIRECTIONS: Read the passage and answer the accompanying questions.

EXPLORE THE CONTEXT: The prayer in the excerpt below (date of origin c. 1500s C.E.) is one to a God of the Inca people. The Inca controlled a vast empire and used a tool called a *quipu* to keep records. The European explorers and missionaries who first encountered the Inca recorded and translated some of their work.

PRIMARY SOURCE: PRAYER

❝ O Pachacamac!

Thou who hast existed from the beginning,

Thou who shalt exist until the end,

powerful but merciful,

Who didst create man by saying,

'Let man be,'

Who defendest us from evil,

and preservest our life and our health,

art Thou in the sky or upon the earth?

In the clouds or in the deeps?

Hear the voice of him who implores Thee,

and grant him his petitions.

Give us life everlasting,

preserve us, and accept this our sacrifice. ❞

—from Three Prayers, *Ancient Civilizations of the Andes* by Philip Ainsworth Means

VOCABULARY

Pachacamac: Inca God of creation
implores: begs
petitions: requests

1 **EXPLAINING** What is the central request of this prayer? What does the speaker ask of Pachacamac?

_____

_____

_____

_____

2 **ANALYZING** How does the speaker describe Pachacamac? What powers are said to belong to this God?

_____

_____

_____

_____

3 HISTORY What type of document is this? How does this fact help you understand these people?

_____

_____

_____

_____

4 **DETERMINING CONTEXT** What details in the prayer help you understand the life of the Inca at the time this document was written?

_____

_____

_____

ESSENTIAL QUESTION

What makes a culture unique?

As you gather evidence to answer the Essential Question, think about:

- how the geography of the region impacted civilization.
- how a society's leaders contribute to its culture.
- the reasons for the collapse of a culture.

My Notes

_____

_____

_____

_____

_____

_____

_____

_____

The Maya

DIRECTIONS: Search for evidence in Chapter 12, Lesson 2 to help you answer the following questions.

1 **ANALYZING** What details about the city of Tikal help reveal information about Maya culture?

_____

_____

_____

_____

_____

_____

_____

_____

2 **HISTORY** Why did the Maya sacrifice humans, and who did they usually sacrifice?

_____

_____

_____

3 **ANALYZING TEXT** What details in the text tell you that women played a significant role in Maya society?

_____

_____

_____

4 HISTORY Use the graphic organizer to take notes about Maya civilization. .

Main Ideas	Notes
Maya Religion	
Social classes	
Achievements	

5 RELATING EVENTS Use the graphic organizer to identify the theories on why Maya civilization collapsed.

Possible Reasons

Maya Collapse

Carved Vessel of the Maya

ESSENTIAL QUESTION
What makes a culture unique?

DIRECTIONS: Study the following image and answer the accompanying questions.

EXPLORE THE CONTEXT: This artifact was found in Mexico and is considered to be from the Maya. It was created between 600 and 900 C.E.

PRIMARY SOURCE: ARTIFACT

1 HISTORY What type of artifact is pictured here? How might it have been used?

_____

_____

_____

_____

2 GEOGRAPHY What natural resources would have been needed to create the artifact? What does that tell you about the geography of the region where it was made?

_____

_____

_____

_____

_____

_____

_____

3 DESCRIBING What details from the design on the vessel help you understand the culture in which it was created?

_____

_____

_____

_____

_____

_____

Diego de Landa on Maya Civilization

ESSENTIAL QUESTION

What makes a culture unique?

DIRECTIONS: Study the following excerpt and answer the accompanying questions.

EXPLORE THE CONTEXT: Diego de Landa was a Franciscan monk sent to the Yucatán in 1549 C.E. His task was to convert the Maya to Catholicism. He learned a great deal about Maya culture and recorded it in many books. This passage is an excerpt from one of those books.

VOCABULARY

inclined: of a mind
reckoning: calculating
sacraments: rituals
omens: signs

divinations: predictions
antiquities: history
esteem: honor

PRIMARY SOURCE: BOOK

❝[The high priests] taught the sons of the other priests, and the second sons of the chiefs, who were brought to them very young for this purpose, if they found them inclined toward this office.

The sciences which they taught were the reckoning of the years, months and days, the festivals and ceremonies, the administration of their sacraments, the omens of the days, their methods of divination and prophecies, events, remedies for sicknesses, antiquities, and the art of reading and writing by their letters and the characters wherewith they wrote, and by pictures that illustrated the writings.

They wrote their books on a long sheet doubled in folds, which was then enclosed between two boards finely ornamented; the writing was on one side and the other, according to the folds. The paper they made from the roots of a tree, and gave it a white finish excellent for writing upon. Some of the principal lords were learned in these sciences, from interest, and for the greater esteem they enjoyed thereby; yet they did not make use of them in public. ❞

— Diego de Landa, *Yucatan Before and After the Conquest*

McGraw-Hill Education: de Landa, Friar Diego. 1937. Translated by William Gates. Yucatan Before And After The Conquest. Publication 20 of The Maya Society. Baltimore: The Maya Society.

Copyright © McGraw-Hill Education

1 HISTORY What type of document is this? How does this help you understand it?

_____

_____

_____

2 ANALYZING What subjects make up the education of a young priest, according to the excerpt? What role do these students probably play in the culture?

_____

_____

_____

3 HISTORY The author includes details about how information is preserved. What can you tell about the culture from the details in the passage?

_____

_____

_____

4 INFERRING What was happening to the Maya people at the time of the writing of the excerpt? How does this information help you understand this document?

_____

_____

_____

ESSENTIAL QUESTION

What makes a culture unique?

1 Think About It

Review the supporting questions you developed at the beginning of the chapter. Review the evidence you gathered in Chapter 12. Were you able to answer each Supporting Question?

If there was not enough evidence to answer your Supporting Questions, what additional evidence do you think you need to consider?

_____

_____

_____

_____

2 Organize Your Evidence

Use a web like the one below to organize the evidence you will use to support your Position Statement.

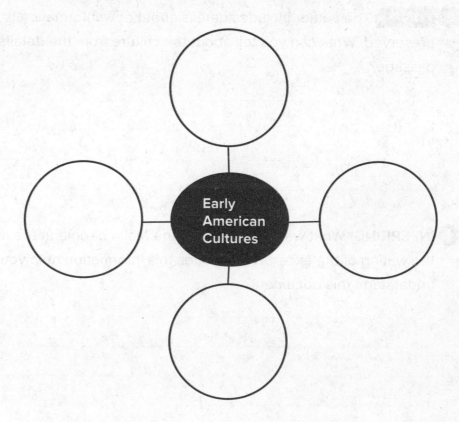

③ Talk About It

Discuss the evidence you have gathered with a small group or partner. Check your group's understanding of the qualities that make a culture unique, and answer any questions members may have. Consider any additional advice or input they may have.

④ Connect to the Essential Question

On a separate piece of paper, write the questions you would like to ask of a person from one or more of the ancient American cultures. Use details from the text to answer those questions as if you were interviewing someone from ancient America. Your questions and answers should address the ESSENTIAL QUESTION: *What makes a culture unique?*

CITIZENSHIP
TAKING ACTION

MAKE CONNECTIONS We know what we do about ancient American cultures because of the work done to preserve the places where they lived. Many of these places are designated as national parks or historic places and protected by the government. Take a "journey" throughout North and South America by visiting the websites of the parks and preserved archaeological sites that contain the remains or evidence of America's oldest peoples. For example, in Colorado, you could visit Mesa Verde National Park to learn about the early cultures that built their homes into cliffs. In Ohio, you could tour parks that preserve the mounds of the ancient Mound Builders. In Mexico, you could visit tourist destinations that have preserved the ancient Maya pyramids. At Machu Picchu in Peru, you could see an ancient Inca site at the highest peaks of the mountains.

DIRECTIONS: Use what you have learned in Chapter 12 about what makes a culture unique to create a travel brochure that focuses on a journey to study the landmarks of ancient American cultures. Your travel brochure should feature at least four landmark destinations in both North and South America. For each landmark destination, your brochure should give information about what to learn from the landmark, the culture that created it, and details about how to access the landmark today, including a cost for a tour, how to get there, and the important things to see on a tour.

_____

_____

_____

_____

_____